Maryland HSA Coach
High School Biology

Coach
America's Best for Student Success

Triumph Learning®

Maryland HSA Coach, High School Biology
63MD
ISBN-10: 1-58620-724-5
ISBN-13: 978-1-58620-724-3

Content Developer: Publisher's Partnership
Cover Image: John Shaw/Taxi/Getty Images

Triumph Learning® 136 Madison Avenue, 7th Floor, New York, NY 10016

Printed in the United States of America.

10 9 8 7 6 5 4

Table of Contents

Maryland Indicators

Introduction to the Student

Every year, the state of Maryland gives a science test to Grade 10 students. The purpose of the test is to find out what you have learned about Biology.

The test is not a test of how many science details you have memorized. It is a test of how well you understand some of the important ideas in science.

This book, the **Maryland Coach, High School Biology**, was written to help you prepare for the test. It will help you in the following ways:

- This book begins with a **Pretest**. Every test item is tied to a benchmark from Maryland State Standards. These benchmarks are what the Maryland High School Biology Test is based on. If you do not answer an item in the Pretest correctly, you can find out which benchmark that item is related to. Then you can study the material under that benchmark when you prepare for the Maryland High School Biology Test.

- The book then presents a lesson for every benchmark in the Maryland Standards. Lessons are divided into units and chapters, following the structure of the Maryland Standards. Every lesson has an Example Question for you to practice using your knowledge. The discussion after each Example Question helps you to understand how to answer the question. That way you can check to see if your own answer is right or wrong.

- Unit I is called Cells and focuses on cells. Unit II focuses on Matter and Energy in the Environment. Unit III focuses on Heredity. Unit IV deals with Organisms and Ecosystems, and Unit V is The Scientific Process. Every unit ends with a Unit Review to further test and review your learning in that unit.

- After the lessons, you can take a **Posttest**, which is similar to the Maryland High School Biology Test in format, kinds of questions, and number or items. Like the Pretest, the Posttest items are tied to benchmarks from the Maryland State Standards, so you can see your areas of strength and weakness.

- The book ends with a Glossary made up of the Key Words that you will see throughout the lessons in the book. They provide a way to quickly review your understanding of the science terminology for this grade level.

Work through the book carefully. Please remember that the concept, or "big idea," behind an answer is more important than the answer itself. There are no short cuts to doing well on the **Maryland High School Biology Test**. Study hard and let the *Maryland Coach, High School Biology* guide you to success. Good Luck!

Maryland Coach, High School Biology Pretest

Pretest

1 What type of organic compound serves to give plants their rigid structures?

   A carbohydrates

   B lipids

   C nucleic acids

   D proteins

2 Which statement is true about water?

   F Water is a weak solvent.

   G Water is a polar molecule.

   H A water molecule is made up of three kinds of atoms.

   J Water has higher density than most other substances.

3 What kinds of molecules are broken down to supply most of the body's energy?

   A proteins

   B lipids

   C carbohydrates

   D nucleic acids

4 A student determines the pH of a solution into which he is placing a cell. Which pH value would indicate that the solution is acidic?

   F 3.1

   G 7.0

   H 8.9

   J 13.8

5 A scientist is conducting an investigation in which she sets up the experiment shown here. The cellophane membrane acts like a cell membrane. Only water molecules can pass from the beaker into the bulb. Both water molecules and glucose molecules can enter the beaker from the bulb. Glucose molecules are larger than water molecules and therefore move across the membrane at a much slower rate.

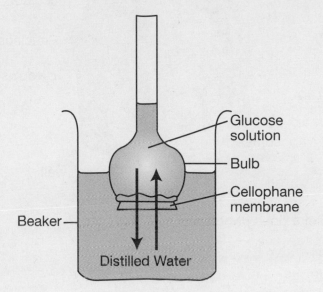

Glucose solution

Bulb

Cellophane membrane

Beaker

Distilled Water

After several days, the scientist observes the height of the liquid in the beaker. Predict whether it will be higher, lower, or the same as it was at the beginning of the experiment. Provide reasons for your prediction.

Write your answer in your Answer Book.

_____

_____

_____

6 Why might a biologist use a catalyst?

F to maintain a steady pH within a cell

G to force two elements to bond together

H to increase the rate of a chemical reaction

J to increase the mass of the molecules in a cell

7 The ability of the human body to regulate its internal temperature is an example of

A osmosis

B respiration

C homeostasis

D binary fission

Directions   Use the diagram of the plant cell to answer Numbers 8 and 9.

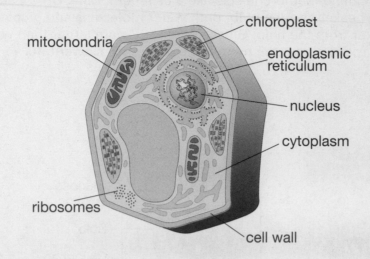

8   In which organelle does photosynthesis take place?

    F   the nucleus

    G   the vacuole

    H   the chloroplast

    J   the mitochondrion

9   In which organelle are amino acids linked together to form proteins?

    A   the vacuole

    B   the ribosome

    C   the chloroplast

    D   the mitochondrion

---

10   Groups of cells are organized into systems that control functions in the body. Examples in the human body include the digestive and respiratory systems. By what main characteristics are cells organized into systems?

    F   similar age

    G   similar size

    H   similar location

    J   similar function

11   The cell membranes of red blood cells contain channels through which glucose molecules can pass without the expense of energy. The glucose moves from an area of high concentration to an area of low concentration.

This is an example of

    A   diffusion

    B   mitosis

    C   fission

    D   active transport

12   *Clostridium tetani* is a type of bacteria that produces a poisonous substance that causes tetanus In the human body. The most common form of the condition is characterized by a locked jaw, stiff neck, and stiff muscles.

The poisonous substance is called

F   a toxin   **H**   a decomposer

G   a parasite   **J**   a mutation

13   Which diagram accurately compares aerobic and anaerobic respiration?

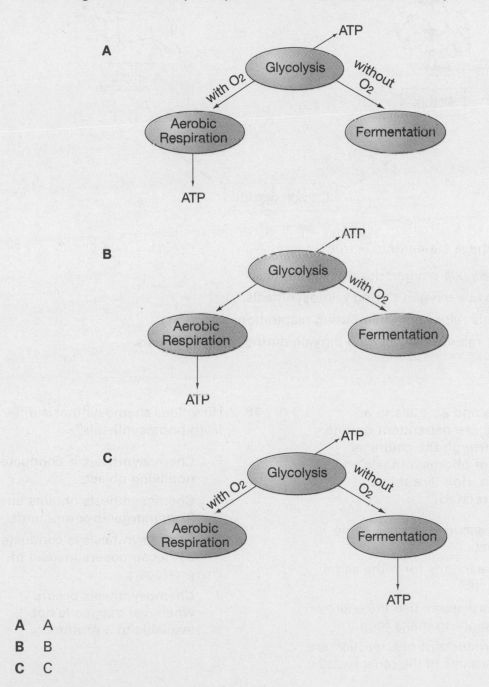

A   A

B   B

C   C

14 The diagram shows the relationship between oxygen and carbon dioxide in an ecosystem.

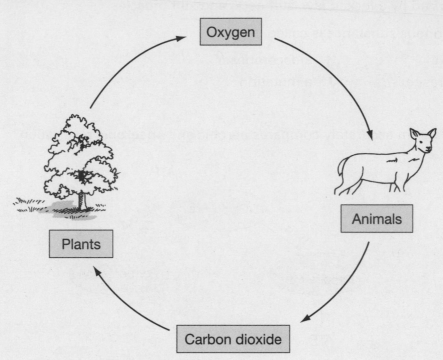

Which of these statements is true?

F   Animals use oxygen during respiration.

G   Plants use oxygen during photosynthesis.

H   Animals release oxygen during respiration.

J   Plants release only carbon dioxide during photosynthesis.

15 The plants and animals in an ecosystem are dependent on one another through the chemical reactions of photosynthesis and respiration. How are these reactions related?

A   Both reactions use the same products.

B   Both reactions form the same products.

C   Both processes use the energy of sunlight to make food.

D   The products of one reaction are the reactants of the other reaction.

16 How does chemosynthesis differ from photosynthesis?

F   Chemosynthesis is conducted by nonliving objects.

G   Chemosynthesis obtains energy from inorganic compounds.

H   Chemosynthesis is conducted by decomposers instead of producers.

J   Chemosynthesis occurs whenever oxygen is not available to a producer.

17 A farmer has decided to raise livestock on his farmland.

- What is the nitrogen cycle?
- How will the farmer's decision alter the nitrogen cycle on his land?

Write your answer in your Answer Book.

_____

_____

_____

_____

_____

18 Which type of cell would be produced as a result of meiosis?

F sperm cell

G liver cell

H blood cell

J heart cell

19 A biologist observed different colors of coats in a population of wild horses. The process that contributes to the variety of coats in the population of horses is

A meiosis

B mitosis

C genetic engineering

D asexual reproduction

20 A body cell of a horse has 64 chromosomes. How many chromosomes are in the unfertilized egg of a female horse?

F 16

G 32

H 64

J 128

21 In guinea pigs, the allele for black coat *(B)* is dominant over the allele for brown coat *(b)*. The Punnett square shows the alleles of two guinea pigs that were crossed.

	B	b
B	BB	Bb
b	Bb	bb

- How does a genotype differ from a phenotype?
- What are the possible genotypes and phenotypes of the offspring?
- Predict the percentages of the offspring that will have each genotype.
- Predict the percentages of the offspring that will have each phenotype.

Write your answer in your Answer Book.

_____

_____

_____

_____

22 When a breeder crossed two black rabbits, 79% of the offspring had black coats and 21% had brown coats. According to these results, the allele for brown coat is

F recessive

G dominant

H sex-linked

J mutated

23 Which of the following can a molecule of DNA **best** be likened to?

A a maze

B a puzzle

C a set of blueprints

D a computer printer

24 What is the role of genes in heredity?

F A gene protects DNA from becoming damaged.

G A gene contains information to determine a single trait.

H A gene transports DNA from the nucleus to the cytoplasm.

J A gene carries amino acids to the place where they are assembled.

25 A strand of DNA contains a section with the following sequence of bases:

TCA   GCA   TAG

What would be the sequence of bases on the complementary strand of DNA?

A GAT   ACG   ACT
B AGT   CGT   ATC
C TCA   GCA   TAG
D TAG   GCA   TCA

26 A cell contains several different types of RNA.

• What are the three main types of RNA?

• How is each form of RNA involved in the production of proteins?

Write your answer in your Answer Book.

_____

_____

_____

_____

27 Which of these is most likely to cause damage to chromosomes?

A acid rain
B radiation
C fertilizer
D methane gas

28 A human cell experiences a mutation in its DNA. What is the most likely change as a result of this event?

F The cell will become part of a different organ system.

G The cell will no longer carry genetic information.

H The cell will produce a different protein.

J The cell will not reproduce.

29 Through which process is a cell produced that is identical to its parent cell?

A mitosis
B succession
C natural selection
D sexual reproduction

30 Genetic engineering is used to produce human insulin. What is involved in this process?

F Genes are destroyed within a chromosome.

G Genes are created artificially in a laboratory.

H Genes are transferred from one organism to another.

I Genes are altered to specify different traits within an organism.

31 Darwin developed his theory of natural selection after studying finches on the Galapagos Islands. He noted that groups of finches had very different beaks.

- How do variations among organisms play a role in natural selection?

Write your answer in your Answer Book.

_____

_____

_____

32 Natural selection could not occur without which of the following processes?

F   cloning

G   genetic engineering

H   ecological succession

J   sexual reproduction

33 Penguins are white on the front and black on the back. When they are swimming, they are at risk from predators. Their coloring helps them because their dark backs blend into the water as seen from above. From below, they are white and are difficult to see against the surface of the sea. Which term best describes this characteristic?

A   recombination

B   homeostasis

C   mutation

D   adaptation

34 A scientist studied a strand of DNA from four species of organisms. The sequences from the DNA strands are shown in the chart.

Species	DNA Sequence
1	GTA ATT TCG
2	GTA GCC ATC
3	ACG CCG TAC
4	GTC GCC ATG

According to the chart, which two of the species of organisms are most closely related?

F 1 and 2

G 2 and 4

H 3 and 4

J 1 and 4

35 Biological evolution means that species undergo changes in their traits over time. Which information would provide the least convincing evidence for the process of evolution?

A The fossil record shows that humans have developed a smaller chin in the last few hundred thousand years.

B Genetic evidence suggests that chimpanzees and humans shared a common ancestor about five to nine million years ago.

C The human hand and whale flipper share a basic common form.

D Humans have moved to warmer climates in response to cold weather.

Directions The information below describes a type of community found in the ocean. Use this information to answer Numbers 36 and 37.

> Living corals can be found near the surface of the ocean water in some warm regions of the world. The corals provide a home for algae. The algae, in turn, produce food that is used by the corals.

36 What type of relationship exists between the corals and the algae?

F predation   H mutualism
G parasitism   J commensalism

37 What is a biotic factor in this ecosystem?

A the temperature of the water
B the salt content of the water
C the size of the algae population
D the amount of sunlight that reaches the coral

Directions Use the diagram to answer Numbers 38 and 39.

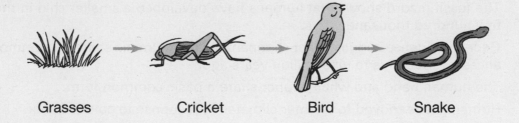

Grasses   Cricket   Bird   Snake

38 The diagram shows a food chain from a terrestrial food web. What does a food chain show?

F the flow of energy
G the migration patterns of organisms
H the stages in the life of various organisms
J the number of organisms at each level within an ecosystem

39 What is the role of the cricket in the ecosystem?

A producer   C decomposer
B consumer   D scavenger

40 A forest habitat has been destroyed by a fire. After a while, new organisms begin to inhabit the area. The first organisms to live in the area are known as the

    F decomposers

    G pioneer species

    H climax community

    J establishers

41 The dorsal fin of a bony fish called a remora is formed in the shape of a suction cup that it uses to attach itself to a shark. When the shark feeds, the remora feeds on the shark's scraps. The shark does not prey on the remora.

A disease causes most of the sharks in a particular region to die. As a result, the remora population will **most likely**

    A take the place of the sharks in the ecosystem

    B increase in size due to the shark's removal

    C decrease in size due to the shark's removal

    D form a feeding relationship with a different animal

42 What is the likely result of habitat destruction caused by human activities?

    F a loss of biodiversity

    G the introduction of new species

    H an increase in bacteria

    J increased precipitation

43 A student is investigating how a human's breathing rate changes when the person goes from rest to activity. A teacher tells the student that the rate should increase by about 60 breaths per minute. How might this information affect the investigation?

    A It might introduce bias.

    B It might increase the precision of the measurements.

    C It might eliminate the need for repeated measurements.

    D It might eliminate any flaws in the design of the experiment.

44 A student wants to determine the pH of a solution surrounding a cell. Which of these would be the best tool for the student to use?

F litmus paper

G thermometer

H compound microscope

J graduated cylinder

45 Which of the following is true about any scientific investigation?

A It should lead to the production of a useful application.

B It should be presented for review and repetition.

C It should show that the hypothesis was correct.

D It should make additional research unnecessary.

46 You are beginning an investigation and you see the following symbol within your procedure. What does this symbol indicate?

Sharp object

F You will be pouring hazardous chemicals.

G You will be working with sharp objects.

H You will be working with open flames.

J You will need an eye wash station.

47 At the turn of the 20th century, a naturalist studied plant species in a particular area. He kept careful records of the plant species he found and the bees that visited them. Seventy-five years later, a group of scientists returned to the area to repeat the naturalist's procedures. They found 74 fewer bee species than the naturalist found. Predict what the scientists found when they counted the plant species.

A fewer than the naturalist counted

B more than the naturalist counted

C about the same number as the naturalist counted

D no remaining plant species in the area

48 This graph shows the temperature of a solution compared with the amount of heat added to it. How many more joules of heat would you expect to need to raise the temperature to 120°C?

Temperature of a Solution

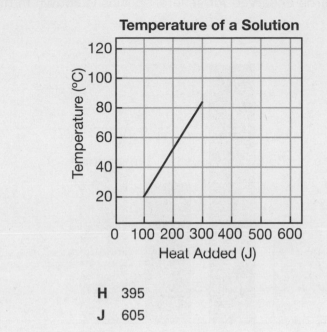

F   105   H   395
G   315   J   605

Directions   Use the illustration and the classification key to answer Number 49.

CLASSIFICATION KEY

1.	a. solid coat	go to 2
	b. not solid coat	go to 3
2.	a. smooth coat, long tail, no mane	*Felis concolor*
	b. smooth coat with a mane	*Panthera leo*
3.	a. striped	*Panthera tigris*
	b. spotted	*Acinonyx jubatus*

49 A scientist created this dichotomous key to study types of wild cats. According to the key, what is the name of this organism?

A   *Felis concolor*   C   *Panthera tigris*
B   *Panthera leo*   D   *Acinonyx jubatus*

Directions Use the information and bar graph to answer Numbers 50 and 51.

A researcher is studying the types of birds living in a section of the Chesapeake Bay Watershed. The number of birds observed for several species is shown in the bar graph.

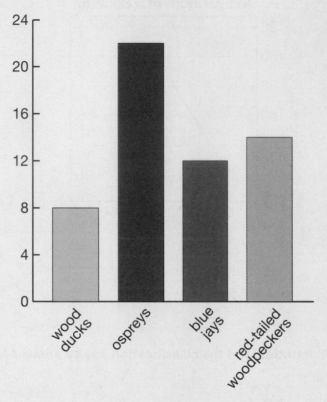

50 Based on the data, what is the ratio of wood ducks to blue jays?

F 3/2

G 1/20

H 2/3

J 4/11

51 The researcher believes that the number of birds in a larger section of the watershed will be proportional to the number observed in the small section. If the researcher observed 70 birds in a larger section, how many wood ducks would he expect to see?

A 1

B 7

C 10

D 54

52 In 2000, the human population reached 6,100,000,000 people. How is this number written in scientific notation?

    F 6.1×10^9

    G 61×10^9

    H 6.1×10^{-9}

    J 61×10^{-9}

53 Nuclear power plants produce waste that is dangerous for many years to come. What is the scientist's role in presenting this issue to the public?

    A   telling people what must be done with the waste

    B   providing funding to dispose of radioactive waste

    C   deciding if nuclear energy is a worthwhile energy resource

    D   explaining radioactivity along with the benefits and dangers of nuclear energy

54 In 1928, Alexander Fleming discovered penicillin after observing that mold inhibited the growth of bacteria in a culture in his laboratory. How did his discovery impact society?

    F   It eliminated bacterial infections.

    G   It protected people from developing bacterial infections.

    H   It provided a way of treating people suffering from bacterial infections.

    J   It showed scientists how to manipulate bacteria to make them less harmful.

55 A group of students is studying samples of rock the students found when investigating their local soil. Each student calculated the density of the rock samples. The tables below show their results.

Student 1
Density (g/mL)
3.54
3.63
3.58
3.59

Student 2
Density (g/mL)
3.184
3.608
2.986
3.901

Student 3
Density (g/mL)
3.24
3.66
3.50
3.89

Student 4
Density (g/mL)
4.04
4.57
4.65
4.21

- Which set of data has the greatest precision?
- The accepted density value for the sample they were measuring is 4.07 g/mL. Which student made the most accurate measurement?
- How is precision different from accuracy?
- What are sources of error that might limit the precision or accuracy of this measurement?

Write your answer in your Answer Book.

_____

_____

_____

_____

_____

_____

_____

Cells

Cells and Organisms

Key Words..........

Cell
Single-celled organism
Multicellular organism
Tissue
Organ
Organ system

The cells in a large organism are not larger than those in a small organism. All cells are basically small. Instead, a smaller organism simply contains fewer cells than a larger organism.

Biology is the study of living things. Despite a variety of sizes, shapes, and other characteristics, all living things have something in common. All living things are made up of basic building blocks called **cells**. Cells range in diameter from 0.0001 mm to about 10 cm. Most cells are shaped like rounded boxes, but they can be flat, long, or any irregular shape.

Some organisms consist of only a single cell. These organisms are known as **single-celled organisms**, or unicellular organisms. In these organisms, one cell carries out all of the functions required to maintain the life of the organism. Bacteria, amoebas, and paramecia are examples of single-celled organisms.

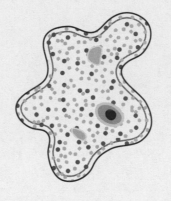

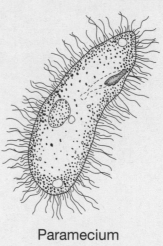

Amoeba   Paramecium

Other organisms are **multicellular organisms**, which means they are made up of many cells. Unlike in a single-celled organism, the cells in multicellular organism are specialized to perform certain functions. In most multicellular organisms, groups of cells are organized into **tissues**. A group of related tissues makes up an **organ**. Organs that work together to perform a set of related tasks form an **organ system**. Together, the organ systems in a multicellular organism carry out the processes necessary to maintain life.

This question asks you to arrange items in order. Reread the question to make sure you know the correct order. Some questions might ask for smallest or simplest to largest or most complex. Other questions might ask for the reverse. Both options are usually among the choices, so be sure you know what you are looking for.

LEVELS OF ORGANIZATION

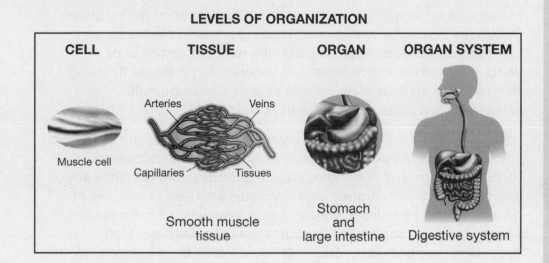

CELL — Muscle cell

TISSUE — Arteries, Veins, Capillaries, Tissues — Smooth muscle tissue

ORGAN — Stomach and large intestine

ORGAN SYSTEM — Digestive system

EXAMPLE QUESTION

Which choice correctly shows the levels of organization in a multicellular organism from simplest to most complex?

A tissue → cell → organ → organ system

B cell → tissue → organ → organ system

C organ system → organ → tissue → cell

D organ → tissue → cell → organ system

DISCUSSION

The cell is the basic building block of a living organism, so it is the simplest structure in a multicellular organism. Cells join together to form tissues, which in turn form organs. A group of organs makes up a system. So choice B is the correct answer.

LESSON 2

Cell Molecules

Key Words...........

Carbohydrate
Protein
Amino acid
Enzyme
Lipid
Nucleic acid
DNA
RNA
ATP

Living things, both single-celled and multicellular, depend on chemical processes that occur within cells. These processes involve organic compounds. The term organic generally refers to compounds containing carbon and hydrogen or substances produced by living things. There are four main classes of organic compounds: carbohydrates, proteins, lipids, and nucleic acids.

Carbohydrates   Perhaps you know that pasta, breads, and fruits contain **carbohydrates**. These are organic molecules composed of carbon, oxygen, and hydrogen. Sugars, starches, and cellulose are examples of carbohydrates. Carbohydrates are used as sources of energy. The carbohydrate glucose, for example, is the main source of energy for cells. Some carbohydrates give structure to living organisms. In plants, the carbohydrate cellulose is a rigid material that supports the plant.

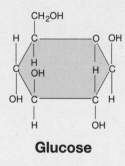

Glucose

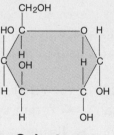

Galactose

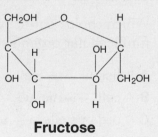

Fructose

Proteins These are organic molecules composed of carbon, hydrogen, and nitrogen. **Proteins** are made up of building blocks called **amino acids.** There are 20 different amino acids that can join together in a tremendous number of different combinations. Some proteins are structural. They serve as the building and binding materials of living things. Collagen, for example, forms bones, tendons, ligaments, and cartilage. Other proteins are functional and take part in chemical reactions, transporting materials, or helping cells move.

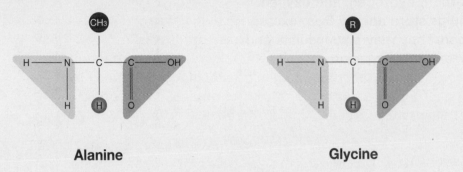

Alanine   Glycine

Some proteins are enzymes. An **enzyme** is an organic catalyst, which is a substance that controls the rate of chemical reactions within cells. Without catalysts, many of the chemical reactions that occur in living things would not be able to occur or would occur at rates that are much too slow for the organism to survive.

Enzymes act upon molecules called substrates. The surface of an enzyme has a distinct shape that allows it to interact with only certain substrates. The enzyme and substrate fit together like a lock and key. A single organism may possess thousands of different enzymes. Each one is specific to a certain chemical reaction.

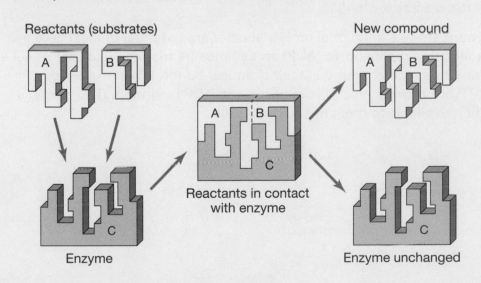

Lipids Fats and oils are examples of **lipids**. These are organic molecules that do not dissolve, or break apart, in water. Lipids are usually found as fats in animals and as oils in plants. Lipids are made up of smaller units known as fatty acids, which consist of carbon, hydrogen, and oxygen. Lipids store energy from excess food. They may also insulate and waterproof organisms.

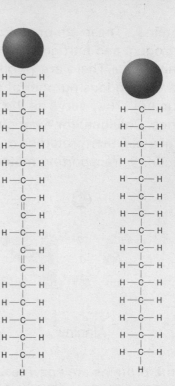

Linoleic Acid **Palmitic Acid**

Nucleic Acids The information that is passed on from one generation of cells to the next—genetic information—is stored in **nucleic acids**. These are large, complex molecules made up of carbon, hydrogen, oxygen, nitrogen, and phosphorous. The two most important nucleic acids are deoxyribonucleic acid (**DNA**) and ribonucleic acid (**RNA**). The genetic information is stored in DNA. It is then translated by RNA and used to direct the production of proteins. (You will learn more about nucleic acids in Unit III.)

There are two additional molecules that are essential to life. These are adenosine diphosphate (**ADP**) and adenosine triphosphate (**ATP**). These molecules store energy in their chemical bonds. When the bonds of ATP are broken, energy is released and ADP is formed. The energy is then available to meet the needs of cells.

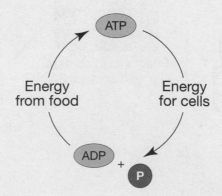

EXAMPLE QUESTION

In living things, protein molecules

A   act as functional and structural components

B   transmit genetic information

C   act as energy-storing molecules

D   provide a source of useable energy for cells

DISCUSSION

Proteins can be structural, functional, or both, so A is the correct choice. Nucleic acids transmit genetic information. Carbohydrates and fats are energy-storing molecules. ATP is a source of usable energy for cells.

Before you read the choices, recall what you know about proteins. Then look for the answer. This will help to prevent you from being distracted by other possible choices.

LESSON

3

The Unique Nature of Water

Key Words..........

Polarity
Solvent
Density

More than one half of your body weight comes from water. It should not surprise you then that water is essential to the survival of living things. Most of the chemical reactions in living things take place in water. Water is also used to transport gases, nutrients, and waste products throughout an organism.

Water's importance to living things arises from its unique properties. One such property is its **polarity**. Each molecule of water consists of two hydrogen atoms and one oxygen atom. Each atom contains positively charged protons and negatively charged electrons. The oxygen atom shares electrons with the hydrogen atoms. However, the electrical charge of the molecule is not evenly distributed. Instead, the oxygen atom pulls the shared electrons toward its center.

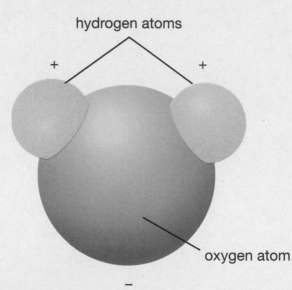

hydrogen atoms

oxygen atom

In addition, the atoms are not arranged in a straight line. The two hydrogen atoms are positioned at an angle to the oxygen atom. The total electrical charge on the molecule is neutral, but the region where the oxygen atom is located has a slightly negative charge. The regions where each of the hydrogen atoms are located have a slightly positive charge. This uneven pattern of charge makes water a polar compound.

32

This polar nature of water makes water a strong solvent. A **solvent** is a substance in which other substances can be dissolved, or broken up. Water is effective at dissolving many other substances. Water dissolves other polar substances, such as sugars and some proteins, as well as other compounds known as ionic compounds. Table salt, or sodium chloride, is an example of an ionic compound.

When an ionic compound is dissolved in water, it breaks up into charged particles called ions. Ions are essential to many biological processes in the body. For example, sodium ions and chloride ions produced when sodium chloride dissolves are involved in the contraction of muscles and the transmission of impulses in the nervous system.

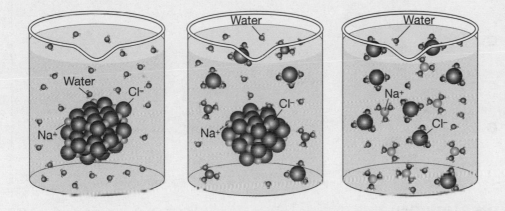

Another important property of water is its **density**. The density of a substance is a measure of its mass divided by its volume. Two objects can occupy the same space but have very different densities. A shoebox filled with feathers, for example, has a much lower density than the same box filled with nickels.

The density of water is 1.00 kg/L, or 1.00 g/cm³. That means that each liter of water has a mass of 1 kilogram. Other substances will float in water if their densities are less than that of water. If the density of a substance is greater than that of water, it will sink in water.

This question involves a choice of four diagrams. In questions like this one, it is often helpful to draw your own diagram first. Then look for the choice that is closest to your drawing.

EXAMPLE QUESTION

Which of these diagrams best represents the shape of a water molecule?

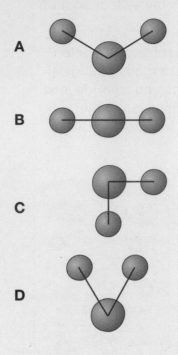

A

B

C

D

DISCUSSION

In a water molecule, the hydrogen atoms are located at angles to the oxygen atom. The atoms are not straight, as in choice B, but they are also not at right angles, as in choice C. The angle is greater than in choice D. Choice A is the correct answer.

LESSON 4

Vitamins and Minerals

Key Words...........

Vitamin
Mineral

In Lesson 2 you learned about four classes of organic compounds required by living things. You then reviewed the importance of water. Living organisms require two additional types of molecules—vitamins and minerals—in order to survive.

Vitamins are organic substances that are necessary in small amounts for the normal functioning of an organism. They enhance the activity of enzymes and help the body perform important chemical reactions. Organisms must be able to obtain vitamins from outside sources. Humans, for example, can obtain Vitamin C from citrus fruit. Vitamins are soluble in either water or fats. The table below summarizes key information about several important vitamins.

Vitamin	Food sources	Deficiency
Water Soluble		
Vitamin B_1	Most vegetables, whole grains, nuts, beans, milk, organ meats	Disturbs the digestive system
Vitamin B_2	Fish, poultry, cheese, yeast, green vegetables, prunes	Causes problems with vision, general weakness, and problems with the skin
Vitamin B_{12}	Meat, poultry, green vegetables, dairy products	Results in a reduced number of red blood cells
Vitamin C	Citrus fruits, tomatoes, strawberries	Results in swollen gums, loose teeth, and bleeding under the skin
Fat Soluble		
Vitamin A	Eggs, liver, carrots, butter, leafy green vegetables	Can lead to night blindness, dry eyes, and infections of the digestive and urinary systems
Vitamin D	Salmon, tuna, fortified milk, cheese	Can result in deformed bones in children, a loss of muscle tone, and poorly formed teeth
Vitamin E	Green leafy vegetables, wheat germ, whole grain cereals	Results in a reduced number of red blood cells and nerve damage in infants
Vitamin K	Leafy green vegetables	Causes blood to clot more slowly, thereby leading to excessive bleeding

Minerals are naturally occurring inorganic substances. They are used to make certain body structures and substances and for normal nerve and muscle function. The minerals calcium and phosphorus are required by teeth and bones. Magnesium, calcium, sodium, potassium, and zinc help regulate the function of nerves and muscles. The table describes several important minerals.

Minerals are not produced by living organisms. Minerals must be replaced on a daily basis, because they are soluble in water. As a result, they are removed from the body through perspiration and excretion.

Vitamin	Food sources	Importance
Iodine	Seafood, iodized table salt	Necessary for the production of thyroid hormones
Cobalt	Green leafy vegetables, liver	Necessary for the synthesis of B_{12}
Zinc	Dairy products, meat, shellfish	Used for the production of digestive enzymes
Molybdenum	Cereals, milk, legumes	Needed for protein synthesis
Manganese	Nuts, whole grains, legumes	Used to produce hemoglobin

Recall from Lesson 2 that enzymes control the rate of chemical reactions. Enzymes are made up of two parts. The protein part of an enzyme is called an apoenzyme. The nonprotein part is called a coenzyme. Vitamins and minerals are usually the coenzymes in one or more enzyme. Vitamin C, for example, is the coenzyme of an enzyme that controls the production of substances that bind the cells of the capillaries together. These are thin vessels through which blood passes. Without Vitamin C, the cells separate and blood leaks out of the capillaries. This is characteristic of a disease called scurvy, which results from a lack of Vitamin C.

EXAMPLE QUESTION

Which of these substances is not considered organic?

A   lipids

B   nucleic acids

C   vitamins

D   minerals

DISCUSSION

Minerals are inorganic substances that are required by living things. Choice D is the correct answer. The other compounds are organic.

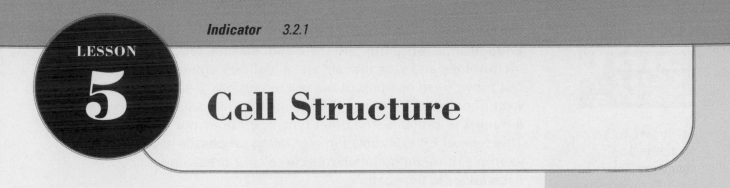

LESSON 5

Cell Structure

The functions carried out by individual cells are completed by specialized structures called **organelles**. The organelles of a plant cell and an animal cell are shown in the diagram below.

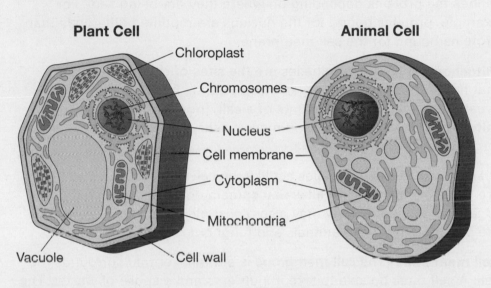

Plant Cell

Chloroplast

Chromosomes

Nucleus

Cell membrane

Cytoplasm

Mitochondria

Vacuole   Cell wall

Animal Cell

Organisms can be divided into two major groups based on the characteristics of the organelles. Organisms whose cells have a membrane-bound nucleus and organelles are called eukaryotes. In other organisms, the genetic information is not contained in a membrane-bound nucleus and neither are the organelles. These organisms are called prokaryotes.

Nucleus   The most obvious structure within the cell is the **nucleus**. This is sometimes described as the control center of the cell. If the nucleus of the cell is removed, the cell will stop growing and die. The nucleus is important because it stores genetic information, which is information that is passed on from one generation to the next. The nucleus is surrounded by a two-layered nuclear membrane. Openings, or pores, in the membrane act as pathways through which materials can flow between the nucleus and the rest of the cell.

Ribosomes   These organelles are the places where proteins are made in the cell. Unlike most other organelles, **ribosomes** are not surrounded by membranes. Ribosomes are formed from proteins and genetic material packed together within the nucleus. Some ribosomes remain free, whereas others attach to the endoplasmic reticulum. Free ribosomes are responsible for forming proteins that will be used within the cell. Proteins that will be inserted into membranes or sent out of the cell are produced on the ribosomes attached to the endoplasmic reticulum.

Cell organelles are located in the **cytoplasm**. This is the area between the cell membrane and the nucleus.

Endoplasmic reticulum (ER) The **endoplasmic reticulum** is a system of membranes and sacs that act like a highway along which molecules can move from one part of the cell to another. One type of ER is dotted with ribosomes. This type of ER is common in cells that make large amounts of proteins. The other type of ER does not have ribosomes. This type of ER is involved in regulating processes in cells. For example, it might maintain muscle cells or break down toxic substances in liver cells.

Golgi Apparatus Proteins move from the ER into the **Golgi apparatus** before they are transported to different parts of the cytoplasm. Like the ER, this organelle is also a system of membranes. It modifies and refines the proteins depending on where they are being sent. For example, proteins bound for the nucleus are modified differently than proteins bound for the cell membrane.

Mitochondria These organelles are the sites of chemical reactions that transfer energy from organic compounds into ATP. The greater the energy requirements of a cell, the more numerous the **mitochondria** will be. Liver and muscle cells, for example, have a large number of mitochondria.

Lysosomes These organelles act like the cell's digestive system. They are small, spherical organelles that contain enzymes that can digest organic compounds. They may also digest old organelles. **Lysosomes** are common in cells of animals and fungi but rare in plant cells.

Cell membrane The **cell membrane** is a thin layer that surrounds the cell. A cell must be able to take in nutrients and dispose of wastes. The cell membrane controls how these substances pass through. The cell membrane is **semipermeable**, which means that some substances can pass through easily whereas others cannot.

In addition to the structures shown on the animal cell, plant cells can have three more structures that are essential to the function of plants.

Cell wall This is a rigid outer layer that surrounds the cell membrane. The **cell wall** makes the cell rigid and protects it from harm. Cell walls contain long chains of cellulose, one of the carbohydrates you read about earlier. Pores in the cell wall allow materials to pass in and out of the cell.

Vacuole This is a fluid-filled organelle that stores enzymes and wastes. Some **vacuoles** can be quite large, taking up about 90 percent of the cell's volume.

Plastid Like mitochondria, **plastids** are surrounded by two membranes and contain genetic material. One type of plastid is the **chloroplast**. Chloroplasts contain the green pigment that is responsible for giving plants their green color.

EXAMPLE QUESTION

Which of the following organelles is involved in the assembling of proteins in animal cells?

A   mitochondria

B   ribosomes

C   plastids

D   lysosomes

DISCUSSION

Proteins are assembled in ribosomes. The correct answer is choice B. Mitochondria are the sites of chemical reactions that transfer energy from organic compounds into ATP. Plastids are found in plant cells. Lysosomes digest organic compounds and old organelles.

LESSON

6

Transportation of Materials

Key Words..........
Diffusion
Osmosis
Passive transport
Concentration gradient
Active transport

In order to carry out the many functions needed to sustain life, cells must be able to take in nutrients. They must also be able to release wastes. One way that materials enter and leave a cell is through **diffusion**. Diffusion is the movement of particles from an area where their concentration is high to an area where their concentration is low. In other words, particles travel from areas where they are crowded to areas where they are less crowded. Because this is the natural movement of particles, diffusion does not require the cell to expend energy.

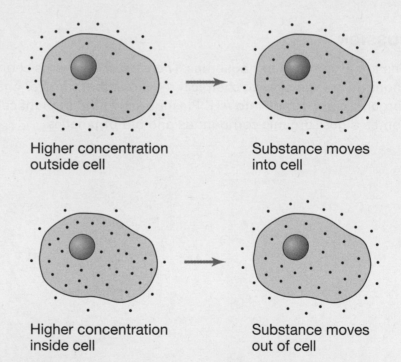

Higher concentration
outside cell

Substance moves
into cell

Higher concentration
inside cell

Substance moves
out of cell

Perhaps the most important substance that passes through the cell membrane is water. Water passes through the cell membrane by a type of diffusion known as **osmosis**. During osmosis, water molecules move from a place of higher concentration to a place of lower concentration—either into or out of the cell.

40

Diffusion is an example of passive transport. In **passive transport**, no energy is needed to move materials into or out of the cell. Passive transport is made possible by the difference in the concentration of particles between two side-by-side regions. This difference in concentration is known as the **concentration gradient**. During passive transport, materials are said to move down the concentration gradient.

In **active transport**, materials move against the concentration gradient. In other words, particles move from a region of lower concentration to a region of higher concentration. This type of movement requires energy. For example, energy is used to actively transport nutrients from the soil into the roots of plants. The plant roots contain a higher concentration of nutrients than the soil. Without active transport, the nutrients would diffuse out of the plant roots into the soil.

Just as cells have methods of transporting materials from one region of the cell to another, multicellular organisms must be able to transport materials as well. For example, vascular tissues in plants move water throughout the plant. In animals, the circulatory system moves blood through the body.

Not all particles can pass through the cell membrane. A cell membrane is selectively permeable, which means that it allows only certain substances to pass through it. Oxygen, water, and food molecules, for example, are able to diffuse into the cell. Waste products, such as carbon dioxide, are allowed to diffuse out of the cell.

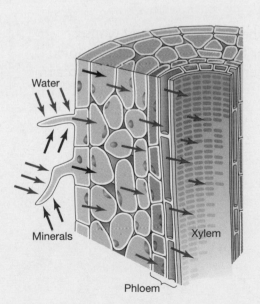

Water

Minerals

Xylem

Phloem

Capillaries of legs

Capillaries of legs

Capillaries of legs

EXAMPLE QUESTION

Each of these cells is placed in a new environment. The cell membranes are permeable to water but not to the particles shown. In which of these situations will water immediately flow into the cell?

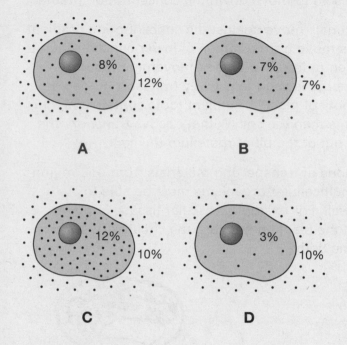

DISCUSSION

Water will flow into the cell when the concentration of water molecules outside the cell is greater than inside the cell. In choice D, the water molecules are more concentrated outside the cell, so some water will move into the cell.

LESSON 7

Reproduction

Key Words...........
Cell cycle
Chromosome
Binary fission
Mitosis
Asexual reproduction
Sexual reproduction
Meiosis

Another process that cells must carry out is the production of more cells. The total number of cells must increase in order for an organism to grow. The process through which a cell forms new cells is known as the **cell cycle**. The cell cycle begins when a cell is formed and ends when the cell divides to form new cells.

Recall that the nucleus of a cell stores genetic information. That information is stored in structures called **chromosomes**. Chromosomes will be discussed in further detail in Unit III. For now, it is important to recognize that the information in a cell's chromosomes must be passed on to any new cells that are produced.

If a cell simply divided into two cells, the resulting cells would have only half the number of chromosomes as the original, or parent, cell. To ensure that each new cell has all of the necessary genetic information, the cell must make a copy of its chromosomes before it divides.

After the genetic information is copied, the actual process of cell division depends on the type of cell involved. In prokaryotic cells, cell division is relatively simple. In this process, known as **binary fission**, a cell splits into two parts. Each part receives one copy of the genetic information. As a result, each new cell is identical to the parent cell. Bacteria reproduce in this way.

Budding is another form of asexual reproduction. In this process, the cytoplasm divides unequally during mitosis. The small cell that results is called a bud.

In eukaryotic cells, the cell cycle is more complex. There are five main stages:

I   The cell grows and carries out routine functions.

II   The cell's chromosomes are copied.

III The cell prepares for the nucleus to divide.

IV   The nucleus divides into two in a process called **mitosis**. Mitosis ensures that each new cell receives a copy of every chromosome.

V   Once mitosis is complete, the cell divides into two cells that are identical to the parent cell.

Cell materials are copied

Mitosis occurs

Cell divides completely

Binary fission and mitosis are examples of asexual reproduction. Reproduction is the process through which organisms produce offspring. **Asexual reproduction** is the production of offspring by a single parent. The offspring produced through asexual reproduction are genetically identical to the parent.

Reproduction in which two parent cells join together to form a new individual is called **sexual reproduction**. If two ordinary cells joined together, the resulting cell would have twice as many chromosomes as it should. This does not happen, because the cells involved in sexual reproduction, known as sex cells (or germ cells), are different from other body cells (called somatic cells). Sex cells have half the number of chromosomes present in other cells of the organism.

Sex cells, also known as gametes, are produced during a process known as **meiosis**. Meiosis is a form of cell division that cuts the number of chromosomes in half. When sex cells are formed, the chromosomes are copied once, but then the nucleus divides twice so that the resulting four cells have half the number of chromosomes found in a normal body cell.

MEIOSIS

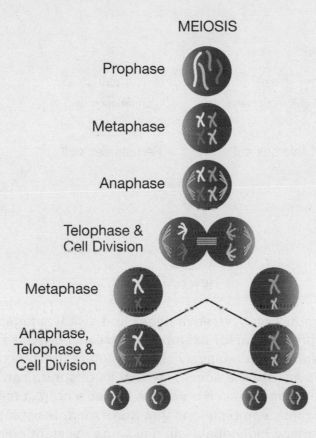

Prophase

Metaphase

Anaphase

Telophase & Cell Division

Metaphase

Anaphase, Telophase & Cell Division

When sex cells combine during a process known as fertilization, the resulting cell has a complete set of chromosomes—half from each sex cell. The offspring of sexual reproduction have a mix of the genetic material from both parents. As a result, they are not identical to either parent.

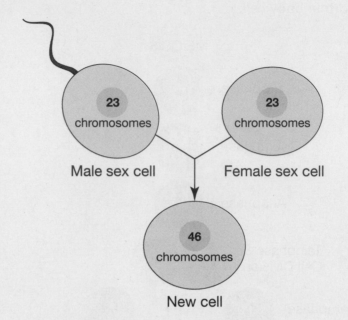

Both forms of reproduction have advantages and disadvantages in nature. Asexual reproduction, for example, enables an organism to produce many offspring in a relatively short period of time. Sexual reproduction, however, has the advantage that its offspring can quickly adapt to new conditions. If a disease strikes a crop, a few plants may have genetic combinations that make them resistant to the disease. While many individuals will die, some resistant plants will survive and reproduce.

Complex organisms have organs specifically for reproduction. In humans, for example, sex cells called sperm cells are produced in male reproductive organs. They are then delivered into the female reproductive system, where organs produce egg cells and support the egg once it is fertilized.

In flowering plants, male reproductive organs called stamens produce pollen, which is required to fertilize ovules produced by female reproductive organs, called pistils.

TEST TAKING STRATEGY

When you need to compare two things, first make a mental note of the primary characteristics of each thing. Then compare the characteristics.

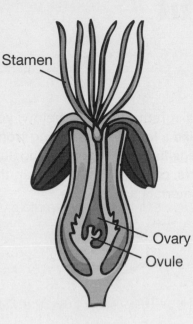

Stamen

Ovary

Ovule

EXAMPLE QUESTION

Compare and contrast mitosis with meiosis.

_____

_____

_____

DISCUSSION

Mitosis and meiosis are both involved in cell division and both result in new cells. However, mitosis produces cells that are identical to the parent cell. Meiosis produces cells that have half the number of chromosomes as each of the parent cells. In both processes, genetic material is copied. However, in mitosis the nucleus divides once, whereas in meiosis the nucleus divides twice.

LESSON 8

Movement

Key Words..........

Flagellum
Cilium

When you look at the diagram of the cell below, you may notice something that looks like a long tail extending from the back. This organelle is called a **flagellum** (pl. flagella). Flagella, along with shorter projections called **cilia** (s. cilium), are involved in the movement of cells or the movement of materials across cells.

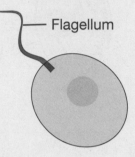
Flagellum

Look at the diagram of male sex cells, known as sperm cells, below. As the flagella whip back and forth, the sperm cells are propelled forward. Flagella on bacteria rotate like propellers. This motion can move a bacterium quite rapidly through its environment. In a similar way, the movement of cilia can propel entire organisms through fluids such as water to search for food or escape predators.

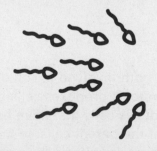

Although you are probably not aware of them, you depend on cilia everyday. The cells lining your respiratory tract are covered by cilia. Particles and debris in the air you breathe become trapped in the cilia. The movement of the cilia pushes these materials to the back of your throat, where they can be removed from the respiratory system.

Movement is also essential to most multicellular organisms. These organisms have organ systems that enable them to move. The diagrams below outline the muscular and skeletal systems of a human. These systems work together to make movement possible.

When a question includes a diagram, take a minute to make sure you know what you are looking at. Identify any and all parts that you can. Then try to answer the question.

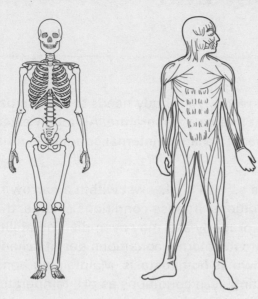

EXAMPLE QUESTION

Which letter points to the cilia of this single-celled organism?

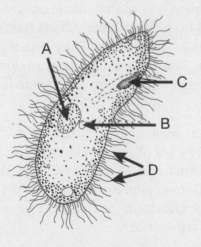

A A

B B

C C

D D

DISCUSSION

Cilia resemble a collection of small hairs. Choice D is correct because this letter points to the small projections from this organism.

LESSON 9

Homeostasis

Key Words...........

Homeostasis
pH
Acid
Base
pH scale

Acids can also be identified using color indicators. An indicator is a compound that changes color when mixed with an acid or a base. One common indicator is litmus paper. It changes from blue to red in an acidic solution.

When you become warm, your body needs to release heat in order to maintain a constant internal temperature. Although external conditions are constantly subject to change, internal conditions must be held relatively constant.

This is true for cells as well. Cells exist within a narrow range of environmental conditions. If those conditions change, the cell may not be able to function properly and may even die. The ability of a cell or organism to regulate its internal conditions despite changes to the environment is known as **homeostasis**. Maintaining homeostasis depends on regulating such conditions as pH, temperature, water level, enzyme operation, light exposure, and gas content.

pH   The **pH** of a substance describes whether the substance is an acid or a base. An **acid** is a substance that is generally recognized by its sour taste. Lemonade tastes sour because it contains citric acid. Vinegar is acidic because it contains acetic acid. A **base** is a substance that can be identified by a bitter taste. Bases feel slippery to the touch and can be poisonous and corrosive. They dissolve fats and oils by reacting to form soap. The base sodium hydroxide is used to clean clogged drains. The base ammonium hydroxide is used as a household cleaner.

The **pH scale** is used to measure the acidity of a solution. The scale ranges from 0 to 14. The pH of an acid is between 0 and 7, whereas the pH of a base is between 7 and 14. The lower the pH of an acid, the stronger the acid is. Conversely, the higher the pH of a base, the stronger the base is. A substance with a pH of 7 is neither an acid nor a base. It is a neutral substance.

pH Scale

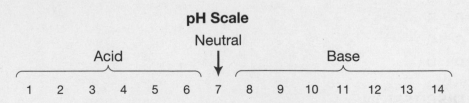

Temperature Temperature describes how hot or cold something is. Most of the chemical reactions in living things are temperature dependent. Changes in temperature cause them to slow down, speed up, or not occur at all. The sum total of the body's chemical activities is known as *metabolism*. The rate at which metabolism occurs describes how fast the body uses energy. Changes in temperature cause changes to the metabolic rate.

Organisms have methods of dealing with changes in temperature. Suppose, for example, that the outdoor temperature drops. Various systems go into action to offset the change. First, the body begins to shiver, which generates heat through muscle movement. Then the circulatory system diverts blood to critical areas, such as the heart. Glands, which are part of the endocrine system, send out signals to increase the body's metabolism. By increasing these processes, the body temperature rises.

Water is an important factor in the regulation of body temperature. Water absorbs heat released by cellular reactions and distributes it throughout the body. When a body becomes warm, it perspires. During this process, a water-based substance evaporates from the skin. During the evaporation process, heat is released from the body.

Not all organisms can produce their own heat. These organisms obtain heat from their environment. Snakes and lizards, for example, bask in the sun to raise their internal temperature or hide in the shade to lower their internal temperature.

Water supply Water is continuously lost through the skin and kidneys. If too much water is lost without being replaced, water moves from spaces between cells into the blood by osmosis. Eventually, water is drawn from the cells as well. When a cell loses water, the materials in the cytoplasm become more concentrated. If they become too concentrated, the cell experiences dehydration and can no longer function. Fortunately, water can be replaced by drinking water or consuming foods, most of which contain water.

DID YOU KNOW?

In some organisms, metabolism slows so much during cold weather that they hibernate.

Enzyme regulation   Recall that enzymes are substances that enable many chemical reactions to occur within living things. The rate of an enzyme reaction depends on pH, temperature, and concentration. For most reactions, the optimum pH is close to 7. Low or high values tend to slow enzyme activity.

Enzymes of different organisms tend to have different optimum temperatures. The optimum temperature in humans, for example, is about 37°C. The optimum temperature in plants is about 25°C. All enzymes are destroyed at temperatures above 50°C.

When pH and temperature are controlled, the concentration of enzyme and substrate molecules affects enzyme activity. If the number of enzyme molecules is fixed and there are more substrate molecules, the reaction rate rises and then levels off. It levels off when all of the available enzymes are being used. The reaction rate also rises and then levels off if the number of enzyme molecules is greater than the number of substrate molecules. It levels off when all of the substrate molecules are reacting.

To maintain pH at the appropriate levels, organisms have substances called *buffers*. A buffer can lower the pH of basic fluid or raise the pH of an acidic fluid as necessary. Buffering systems in the body maintain many fluids at normal pH levels.

In addition to the properties of a cell's normal environment, other factors can affect the cells as well. Two important examples are radiation and toxins. *Radiation* is energy in the form of electromagnetic waves, such as X-rays and gamma rays. Radiation causes particles called electrons to be removed from atoms within cells. The resulting charged particles, or ions, react with other atoms to cause damage within the cell.

Cells are exposed to some level of radiation every day. Cells are able to repair any damage caused by low doses of radiation. However, when exposed to higher doses of radiation, the cells become permanently damaged and may even die. In some cases, these cells are simply replaced. In others, these cells go on to produce additional damaged cells. This process may lead to cancerous tumors. In others, it can lead to radiation sickness. This occurs when the body cannot replace cells quickly enough. As a result, entire tissues fail to function and eventually the entire organism can die.

A *toxin* is generally any poisonous substance that can harm a living organism. Some toxins exist naturally, such as substances produced by certain bacteria. Others are produced synthetically, such as wastes produced during some industrial processes. Some toxins attack cells and kill them. Others destroy the cell membrane, causing the cell to leak and die. Still others attack the substrates of enzymes, preventing the enzymes from functioning.

In the following unit, you will learn how cells depend on light for processes known as photosynthesis and cellular respiration. Cells and organisms respond to changes in light exposure in order to survive. Plants, for example, can grow toward a source of light.

EXAMPLE QUESTION

Which of these is a substance that maintains the pH of an environment in a living thing?

A toxin

B mineral

C buffer

D substrate

DISCUSSION

Choice C is the correct answer. A buffer is a substance that offsets changes in pH.

Review

1 Which organic molecule stores hereditary information?

    A   carbohydrates

    B   lipids

    C   proteins

    D   nucleic acids

2 Which of the substances listed in the table will float in water?

Material	Density (g/cm³)
Sucrose	1.59
Copper	8.92
Lead	11.35
Cork	0.24

    F   sucrose

    G   copper

    H   lead

    J   cork

3 In the diagram of the cell, what is the label given to the organelle that transfers energy from organic compounds to ATP?

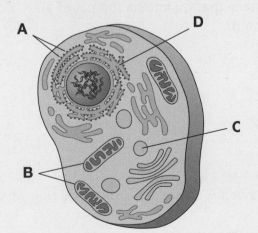

    A   A

    B   B

    C   C

    D   D

4 Which of the cell's features indicates that this is an animal cell?

    F It has a nucleus.

    G It has a cytoplasm.

    H It does not have a cell wall.

    J It is not attached to similar cells.

5 A cell is placed in a new solution. The diagram shows the concentration of substances inside and outside the cell. The cell membrane is not permeable to these substances. Which of these statements best describes what will immediately happen to the cell in the solution?

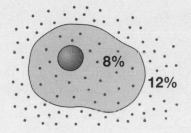

    A Water will move out of the cell.

    B Water will move into the cell.

    C Substances will move out of the cell while water moves into the cell.

    D Substances will move into the cell.

6 Select two vitamins from the following list and explain why they are important and where they can be obtained.

      Vitamin A, Vitamin B$_1$, Vitamin C, Vitamin D, Vitamin E, Vitamin K

Write your answer in your Answer Book.

_____

_____

_____

_____

7   Which of the following processes is required for sexual reproduction?

F   binary fission
G   budding
H   mitosis
J   meiosis

8   What is the role of a cell's flagellum?

A   to take in food
B   to excrete waste
C   to give support to the cell
D   to enable the cell to move

9   A scientist measured the pH of four fluids in an organism. Which fluid is a strong acid?

F   13.4
G   8.2
H   7.0
J   2.3

10   The ability to maintain a relatively constant internal temperature is an example of

A   inheritance
B   homeostasis
C   passive transport
D   metabolism

Matter and Energy in the Environment

LESSON

10

Photosynthesis

All living things need to take in nutrients—food—in order to survive. In most ecosystems, plants are responsible for producing food. For this reason, plants are known as producers. The process through which plants produce food is called **photosynthesis**.

Photosynthesis is a chemical reaction in which carbon dioxide from the air is combined with water in the presence of sunlight to produce organic compounds and oxygen. The organic compounds include the carbohydrate glucose. This chemical reaction is summarized by the chemical equation below.

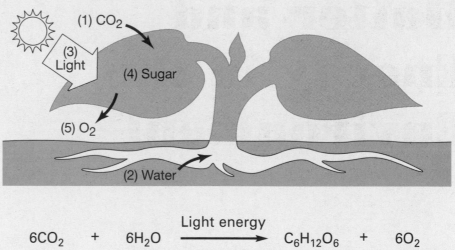

(1) CO_2
(3) Light
(4) Sugar
(5) O_2
(2) Water

$$6CO_2 \quad + \quad 6H_2O \quad \xrightarrow{\text{Light energy}} \quad C_6H_{12}O_6 \quad + \quad 6O_2$$

Carbon dioxide   Water   Glucose   Oxygen

In a chemical equation, the substances written to the left of the arrow are called the **reactants**. The substances written to the right of the arrow are called the **products**. During the chemical reaction, the atoms of the reactants are rearranged to form the products, which have different physical and chemical properties.

Energy is required for photosynthesis. The energy comes from sunlight. During photosynthesis, light energy is converted into chemical energy. This chemical energy is stored in the bonds that hold atoms together. In other words, the energy is stored in the food produced during photosynthesis.

The producers in most ecosystems conduct photosynthesis. However, there are some producers that do not use sunlight to produce food. Some bacteria produce food by using energy stored in inorganic molecules. Many species of archaebacteria, for example, obtain carbon from carbon dioxide and energy from sulfur to produce organic molecules. This process is known as **chemosynthesis**.

If several answer choices seem logical to you and you cannot decide which one is correct, go back to the question and think about the process mentioned. Try to recall what occurs in the process before you read through the choices again. This will help you to eliminate the incorrect choices.

EXAMPLE QUESTION

What occurs during the process of photosynthesis?

A   Chemical energy is converted into light energy.

B   Light energy is converted into chemical energy.

C   Glucose is broken down to release energy.

D   Carbon dioxide and energy are released into the atmosphere.

DISCUSSION

Photosynthesis is the process during which plants make food. Plants, which are autotrophs, use light energy to convert carbon dioxide and water into glucose and oxygen. This process is the conversion of light energy to chemical energy. Choice B is the correct answer.

LESSON 11

Cellular Respiration

Key Words...........

Cellular respiration
Glycolysis
Anaerobic
Aerobic

Different types of respiration do not occur in the same site within a cell. Anaerobic respiration occurs within the cytoplasm of a cell. Aerobic respiration occurs within the mitochondria.

During photosynthesis, which you read about in the previous lesson, plants convert light energy into chemical energy. That energy is stored in carbohydrates and other organic compounds. Both plants and animals use this energy to run activities within cells. They release this energy through a process known as **cellular respiration**.

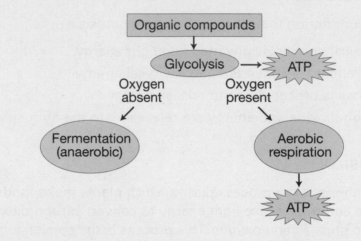

Cellular respiration begins with a process called **glycolysis**. During glycolysis, a molecule of glucose is used to produce two molecules of a substance called pyruvic acid. A small amount of ATP is formed at the same time.

The products of glycolysis can then follow one of two paths depending upon whether or not oxygen is present. If oxygen is not present, the products of glycolysis enter fermentation paths that do not produce additional ATP. A process that occurs without oxygen is an **anaerobic** process.

There are two important types of fermentation. During lactic acid fermentation, an enzyme converts pyruvic acid into a compound called lactic acid. This type of fermentation is used to manufacture certain foods, such as yogurt and cheese. It also occurs in your muscles during strenuous exercise. During another type of fermentation known as alcoholic fermentation, some single-celled organisms convert pyruvic acid into ethyl alcohol. This type of fermentation is used to produce beverages such as wine and beer as well as bread.

Most cells do not undergo fermentation. Instead, if oxygen is present, the products of glycolysis enter **aerobic** pathways. The term aerobic refers to a process that requires oxygen. During aerobic respiration, a great deal of ATP is formed. In fact, aerobic respiration produces almost 20 times as much ATP as glycolysis alone.

The complete process of aerobic respiration is summarized by the equation below.

$$C_6H_{12}O_6 + 6O_2 \longrightarrow 6CO_2 + 6H_2O + Energy$$

Glucose   Oxygen   Carbon dioxide   Water

According to this equation, you can see that during cellular respiration, organisms use organic compounds and oxygen to produce carbon dioxide and water.

Do you notice anything about this equation? This equation is the opposite of the equation describing photosynthesis. In other words, the reactants in this equation were the products in the equation for photosynthesis. And the products in this equation were the reactants in the equation for photosynthesis.

EXAMPLE QUESTION

Which of the following is a product of cellular respiration?

A   oxygen

B   carbon dioxide

C   glucose

D   sunlight

DISCUSSION

A product is a substance formed during a chemical reaction. During cellular respiration, organisms use organic compounds and oxygen to form carbon dioxide and water. Choice B is the correct answer. Choices A and C are reactants, or substances used in a chemical reaction. Choice D is a requirement for photosynthesis.

TEST TAKING STRATEGY

When you read through a question, it might help to underline any key terms. For example, underline the word *product*. Then make sure you recall the definition of the term before you try to answer the question.

DID YOU KNOW?

In any natural process, energy is neither created nor destroyed. Instead, energy is converted from one form to another. During photosynthesis, light energy from the sun is converted into chemical energy stored in the bonds of organic compounds. During cellular respiration, that energy is made available to be converted to other forms, such as thermal energy to maintain an animal's body temperature or mechanical energy to enable an animal to move.

LESSON 12

The Carbon Cycle

Key Words...........

Carbon cycle

A nutrient is an element or compound that organisms need to carry out their life functions. The supply of nutrients in an ecosystem is limited, so the nutrients must be recycled.

As you have learned, the products of photosynthesis become the reactants of cellular respiration. And the products of cellular respiration become the reactants of photosynthesis. Photosynthesis and cellular respiration are related in a continuous cycle known as the **carbon cycle.** Through this cycle, nutrients flow between living systems and the physical environment. Carbon is an important nutrient in most ecosystems.

The diagram below shows how the carbon cycle might exist in one ecosystem. Here you can see that during photosynthesis, plants make food. Recall that during this process, they use the energy of sunlight to convert carbon dioxide and water into organic compounds and oxygen. As a result, plants remove carbon from the atmosphere and store it in organic compounds. At the same time, they release oxygen into the atmosphere.

Both plants and the animals that eat plants conduct cellular respiration. In the process, they release carbon dioxide into the atmosphere and remove oxygen from the atmosphere.

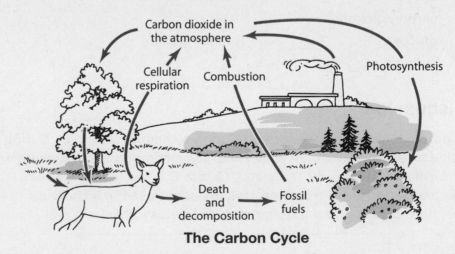

The Carbon Cycle

What happens when an organism dies? You might think that the carbon trapped in its body is removed from the carbon cycle. This is not the case. A group of organisms known as decomposers breaks down dead and decaying matter. In this way, decomposers return carbon to the carbon cycle. (You will read more about decomposers in Unit IV.)

In addition to living organisms, there are other processes at work in the carbon cycle. Perhaps the most important process is combustion. During combustion, fuels are burned. As they burn, oxygen is consumed and carbon dioxide is released into the atmosphere.

Much of the carbon that is burned as a fuel source was locked into fossil fuels such as coal and petroleum millions of years ago. Ancient plants were gradually changed into fossil fuels as a result of high pressures and temperatures. The carbon in their bodies was then locked in the resulting fuels. That carbon is released when the fuels are burned.

EXAMPLE QUESTION

In some parts of the world, rain forests are being cut down to make land available for homes, businesses, and farms. How does the loss of these trees impact the carbon cycle?

A   It causes oxygen to be added to the atmosphere.

B   It decreases the amount of carbon removed from the atmosphere.

C   It increases the amount of carbon removed from the atmosphere.

D   It decreases the amount of fossil fuels produced.

DISCUSSION

Trees are plants that remove carbon from the atmosphere and produce oxygen. If trees are eliminated, less carbon is removed and less oxygen is produced. Choice B is the correct answer.

LESSON
13

The Nitrogen Cycle

Key Words...........

Nitrogen cycle

You can see that throughout the nitrogen cycle, the element nitrogen is continuously combined and recombined in different ways in living things. Bacteria make the cycle possible. Without them, the supply of nitrogen would quickly be depleted.

Another important nutrient in most ecosystems is nitrogen. Organisms require nitrogen in order to produce proteins. Nitrogen is moved through an ecosystem during the **nitrogen cycle**. The illustration shows how the nitrogen cycle might exist in an ecosystem.

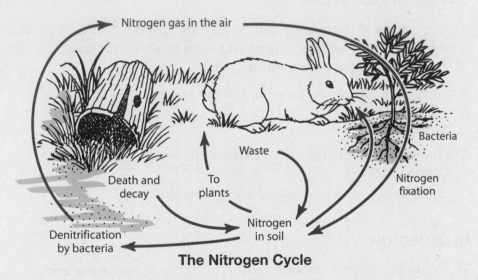

The Nitrogen Cycle

Almost 80 percent of Earth's atmosphere consists of nitrogen. The free form in which it is found in the atmosphere, however, cannot be used by most organisms. Instead, the nitrogen must be changed into compounds called nitrates by nitrogen-fixing bacteria in the soil in a process known as *nitrogen fixation*. Plants then use the nitrates to make amino acids and proteins. (Recall that amino acids are the building blocks of proteins.) Animals that eat the plants obtain the amino acids from the plant proteins. They then make animal proteins from the amino acids.

Like carbon, nitrogen does not become locked within animals and plants when they die. Instead, nitrogen is returned to the soil when plants and animals decay. Ammonia, which contains nitrogen, is produced when their bodies are decomposed. Ammonia is also present in animal wastes. In the process of *denitrification*, certain bacteria change ammonia into free nitrogen, some of which is released into the air. Other bacteria convert ammonia into compounds called nitrites, which are converted in nitrates that plants can use. This begins the cycle again.

Like other cycles, the nitrogen cycle can be upset by changes in an ecosystem. If bacteria in the soil are killed or removed, for example, nitrogen cannot be converted into a useable form and cannot be returned to the cycle. Similarly, if organisms are removed from an ecosystem, their wastes and decay are removed as well. This too upsets the cycle. One major factor in the nitrogen cycle is human activity. When humans enter an ecosystem to build factories, homes, and roadways, for example, they remove plants, soil, and animals. As a result, the amount of nitrogen flowing through the ecosystem is severely altered.

Humans are part of the local and global ecosystem. Any organism can affect its ecosystem for good or for bad. Humans, however, have an especially powerful effect because they have harnessed energy and developed technologies that change the natural flow of nutrients and energy.

EXAMPLE QUESTION

Free nitrogen in the air is changed to nitrogen-containing compounds that can be used by living things in a process called

A   nitrification

B   photosynthesis

C   nitrogen fixation

D   respiration

DISCUSSION

Nitrogen fixation is the process through which bacteria change nitrogen gas into nitrogen-containing compounds that can be absorbed by plants. Choice C is correct.

The Water Cycle

Key Words...........

Water cycle
Evaporation
Transpiration
Condensation
Precipitation

Most organisms are made primarily of water. As a result, water is vital to the survival of most organisms. The **water cycle** describes the constant movement of water through the environment and living things and back again. The illustration below summarizes the water cycle.

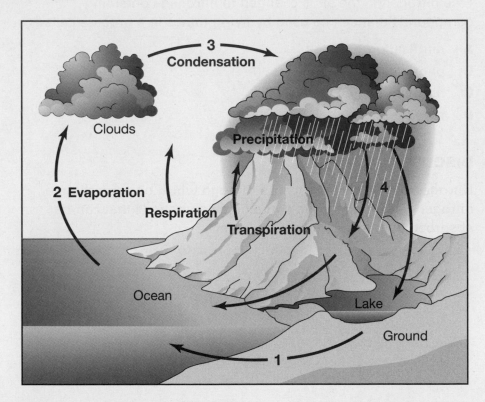

Water enters the atmosphere through three basic processes: evaporation, respiration, and transpiration. **Evaporation** is the process through which water changes from the liquid state to the gas state (water vapor) when it is heated. Respiration, as you learned in Lesson 11, is the process through which organic compounds are broken down. Water vapor is released in the process. **Transpiration** is the process through which water evaporates through openings in plant leaves.

Water is returned from the atmosphere through condensation and precipitation. **Condensation** is the process during which water changes from the gas state to the liquid state when it loses heat energy. Water vapor in the atmosphere condenses into droplets that make up clouds. When the droplets become heavy enough, they fall as precipitation. **Precipitation** is rain, snow, sleet, and hail.

TEST TAKING STRATEGY

When a question requires that you select one answer, first eliminate any answers that you know are incorrect. Then select the correct answer from the remaining choices.

EXAMPLE QUESTION

Which process returns water to Earth's surface?

A   evaporation

B   respiration

C   transpiration

D   precipitation

DISCUSSION

Precipitation is the process through which water falls to Earth's surface as rain, snow, sleet, or hail. Choice D is the correct answer. Water leaves Earth's surface through the other three processes.

Review

1 The products of photosynthesis are

   A   oxygen, water, and energy

   B   glucose and carbon dioxide

   C   oxygen and glucose

   D   carbon dioxide, water, and energy

2 How is light energy involved in photosynthesis?

   F   It is produced.

   G   It is converted.

   H   It is destroyed.

   J   It is magnified.

3 Which process takes place in the presence of oxygen and produces nearly twenty times as much ATP as glycolysis alone?

   A   photosynthesis

   B   lactic acid fermentation

   C   aerobic respiration

   D   mitosis

4 The cellular process that takes place without oxygen and does not produce ATP is

   F   photosynthesis

   G   fermentation

   H   aerobic respiration

   J   glycolysis

5 The diagram shows the relationship between oxygen and carbon dioxide in an ecosystem.

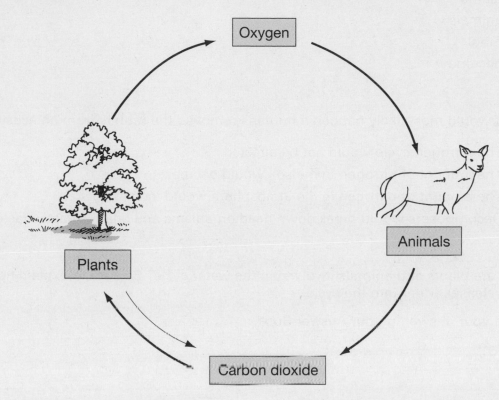

Which of these statements is true?

    A   Animals use oxygen during respiration.

    B   Animals release oxygen during respiration.

    C   Plants release carbon dioxide during photosynthesis.

    D   Plants use oxygen during photosynthesis.

6 Which of these processes removes carbon from the atmosphere?

    F   combustion of fuels

    G   fermentation

    H   cellular respiration

    J   formation of fossil fuels

7   What types of organisms convert free nitrogen into a useable form?

A   plants

B   animals

C   fungi

D   bacteria

8   What would most likely happen if humans removed the rabbits from an ecosystem?

F   The nitrogen cycle would not be affected.

G   The amount of nitrogen in the soil would decrease.

H   The amount of nitrogen in the atmosphere would increase.

J   Decomposers would break down dead organisms and animal wastes faster.

9   How are plants and animals involved in the water cycle? Be sure to explain how each one releases water into the cycle.

Write your answer in your Answer Book.

_____

_____

_____

_____

_____

10   Through which physical change does water vapor in the air form droplets?

A   condensation

B   transpiration

C   evaporation

D   respiration

Unit III

Heredity

LESSON

15

Genes and Chromosomes

Key Words...........

Chromosome
Homologous
chromosomes
Sex chromosome
Autosome
Gene

One trait of living things is the ability to reproduce, or produce new generations of the same species. During reproduction, genetic information is transferred from parents to offspring.

Recall from Lesson 2 that genetic information is stored in DNA. DNA, in turn, is stored in structures called **chromosomes**. In prokaryotic cells, the chromosomes are made up of long, circular molecules of DNA. In eukaryotic cells, the chromosomes are made up of distinct lengths of DNA.

Before mitosis begins, a copy of each chromosome is made. (Recall mitosis from Lesson 7.) The original chromosome and its copy are called chromatids. They are attached to each other by a centromere, as shown in the diagram below. During the process of cell division, the chromatids separate and each new cell receives one.

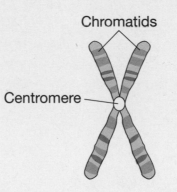

Chromatids

Centromere

Every organism has a characteristic number of chromosomes in its cells. The number of chromosomes is not necessarily related to the complexity of the organism. The table below shows the number of chromosomes in the cells of several different organisms.

Organism	Number of Chromosomes	Organism	Number of Chromosomes
Cat	32	Garden pea	14
Chimpanzee	48	Corn	20
Dog	78	Mosquito	6
Cow	60	Honeybee	32
Human	46	Sugarcane	80
Horse	64	Sand dollar	52

The number of chromosomes in the sex cells, or gametes, of an organism is half the number of chromosomes in the other cells of an organism. Recall that the number of chromosomes is cut in half during meiosis. This makes it possible for sex cells to combine during sexual reproduction to produce cells with the normal number of chromosomes.

As a result of meiosis, an offspring receives one set of chromosomes from the mother and one set from the father. The same types of chromosomes pair together. So, for example, a human skin cell has 23 pairs of chromosomes. Chromosomes that are similar in size, shape, and genetic material are called **homologous chromosomes**. Thus, a human skin cell has 23 pairs of homologous chromosomes.

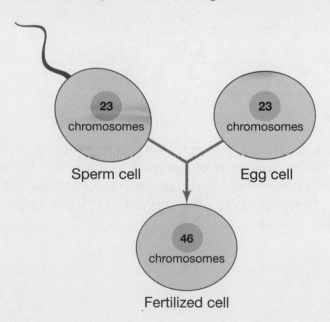

23 chromosomes

Sperm cell

23 chromosomes

Egg cell

46 chromosomes

Fertilized cell

During meiosis, homologous chromosomes pair up and crossover may occur. During crossing-over, portions of a chromatid on one homologous chromosome are broken and switched with the matching portions on one of the chromatids of the other homologous chromosome. Crossing-over increases the number of genetic combinations that can occur in the offspring of sexual reproduction.

Chromosomes are divided into two groups: **sex chromosomes** and **autosomes**. Sex chromosomes determine the sex of an organism and may also carry genes for some characteristics. In humans and many other organisms, the X chromosome is the female chromosome and the Y chromosome is the male chromosome. Human females have two X chromosomes, whereas human males have one X chromosome and one Y chromosome. Autosomes determine characteristics that do not include gender.

If you compare the number of inherited traits of an organism with its number of chromosomes, you will find that there are many more traits than there are chromosomes. Only a small portion of each chromosome determines a specific trait. The section of a chromosome that codes for a single trait is called a **gene**. Each chromosome contains many genes.

The main function of genes is to control the production of a protein. Recall that proteins determine the characteristics of an organism. The specific kind and number of proteins in an organism determine the specific characteristics of that organism.

EXAMPLE QUESTION

Why are offspring of sexual reproduction genetically different from their parents?

_____

_____

_____

_____

DISCUSSION

During sexual reproduction, two sex cells join together to form a new cell. Each sex cell has one copy of genetic information. Therefore, the offspring has half its genetic information from one parent and half from the other. That makes the offspring different from either parent.

LESSON 16

Genotypes and Phenotypes

Generally, the gene for a particular trait contributed by one parent is on one chromosome in the pair. The gene contributed for the same trait by the other parent is on the other chromosome in the pair. The genes are in matching positions on the homologous chromosomes. If the matching genes control contrasting characteristics of a trait, such as tall height and short height, the genes are called **alleles**.

Key Words..........

Allele
Dominant
Recessive
Homozygous
Heterozygous
Genotype
Phenotype

Homologous Chromosomes

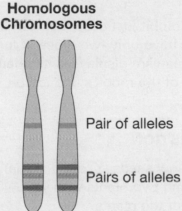

Pair of alleles

Pairs of alleles

If two similar alleles for a characteristic are present, the offspring exhibits that characteristic. But what happens when the offspring receives two different alleles? When this happens, the **dominant** allele is expressed. The other characteristic, the **recessive** allele, is not expressed. Recessive alleles are expressed only when no dominant alleles are present. The table below lists some dominant and recessive traits in humans.

Trait	Dominant	Recessive
Hair type	Curly (wavy) hair	Straight hair
Hair color	Dark	Light
Ear lobe	Free	Attached
Tongue movement	Ability to roll sides	Inability to roll sides
Ability to taste PTC (phenylthiocarbamide)	Tasting	Nontasting

TEST TAKING STRATEGY

Pay attention to words such as *always*, *best*, and *must* when you see them in a question. In this question, some of the choices are possible answers, but they will not be true in every situation.

Dominant alleles are represented with an uppercase letter, and recessive alleles are represented with a lowercase letter. For example, black fur is dominant over brown fur in a certain type of rabbit. A rabbit could be described as BB (two dominant alleles), Bb (one dominant allele and one recessive allele), or bb (two recessive alleles). Remember that the recessive trait, brown fur, appears only when there are no dominant alleles present. So a rabbit will have black fur if it is BB or Bb. It will have brown fur only if it is bb.

An organism that has two dominant or two recessive alleles for a trait is said to be **homozygous**. An organism is called **heterozygous** if it has one dominant and one recessive allele for a trait.

The alleles that an organism inherits from its parent make up the organism's **genotype**. In other words, an organism's genotype is its genetic composition. The possible genotypes of this type of rabbit are BB, Bb, or bb.

Even though the rabbit just described can have three different genotypes, it can have only two types of fur—black or brown. The form of the trait the organism displays is its **phenotype**. Black fur and brown fur are examples of the rabbit's phenotype.

EXAMPLE QUESTION

In pea plants, yellow seeds (Y) are dominant over green seeds (y). A scientist is studying two plants with yellow seeds. Which information must be true about the plants?

A The plants have the same genotype.

B The plants have different genotypes.

C The plants have the same phenotype.

D The plants have different phenotypes.

DISCUSSION

Choice A seems correct, but plants with YY or Yy genotypes will have yellow seeds. For the same reason, choice B does not have to be correct. Both plants might have the same genotype. Choice C is the correct answer. The phenotype is the trait that is expressed. Both plants express the trait of yellow seeds. For the same reason, choice D is incorrect.

LESSON 17

Punnett Squares

Key Words..........

Punnett square
Probability

Scientists can study possible genotypes and phenotypes using a diagram called a **Punnett square**. To create a Punnett square, divide a square into four sections. Write the letters that represent the alleles of one parent across the top of the square. Write the letters that represent the alleles of the other parent down the side of the square.

Combine the alleles from one parent with those from the other in every combination. The example below shows a cross between a brown guinea pig (bb) and a black guinea pig (BB). The B stands for the dominant allele and the b stands for the recessive allele.

Follow the arrows in the example to see how the alleles are combined in each box. Note that the dominant allele is always written first when it is present.

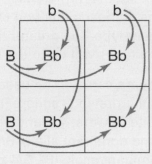

A Punnett square does not give exact information about the offspring. Instead, it provides a **probability**. A probability is the mathematical chance that an event will occur. Look at the Punnett square below. It shows a cross between two heterozygous pea plants with purple flowers. P stands for dominant purple flowers, and p stands for recessive white flowers.

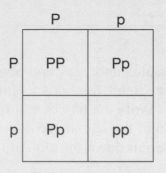

	P	p
P	PP	Pp
p	Pp	pp

The probability that a particular offspring will have the genotype PP is 1 out of 4, or 1/4. To express this relationship as a percentage, divide the numerator by the denominator. Then multiply the answer by 100 percent.

1/4 × 100% = 25%

This does not mean that if there are 100 offspring, exactly 25 will have the PP genotype. It means that you can logically predict that about 25 will have this genotype. The greater the number of offspring, the closer the actual percentages will be to the predicted percentages.

The Punnett square can also be used to analyze the possible phenotypes. In the previous square, there are two phenotypes—purple flowers and white flowers. A plant will have purple flowers as long as it has at least one dominant allele. Because 3 out of the 4 boxes contain one dominant allele (P), 3/4 or 75 percent of the offspring will have purple flowers.

Now look at the Punnett square below. It shows a cross between a tall pea plant (TT) and a short pea plant (tt).

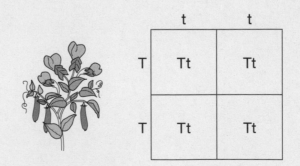

	t	t
T	Tt	Tt
T	Tt	Tt

This Punnett square shows one possible genotype. All of the offspring will be heterozygous. As a result, there is also only one possible phenotype. All of the offspring will be tall. A plant would have to have two recessive alleles to be short. So the probability that the offspring will be tall is 100 percent. The probability that the offspring will be short is 0 percent.

EXAMPLE QUESTION

In rabbits, the allele for black coat color (B) is dominant over the allele for brown coat color (b). Two black rabbits (Bb) are mated. What can you predict about the offspring?

A   Most of the offspring will be brown.

B   Most of the offspring will be black.

C   All of the offspring will be black.

D   All of the offspring will be brown.

DISCUSSION

A Punnett square is helpful when making predictions about the offspring of a cross. If you create a Punnett square for this question, you should use two parents that have the same genotype (Bb). The possible genotypes of the offspring are BB, Bb, and bb. Only the offspring with the bb genotype will be brown. So only about 1/4 or 25 percent of the offspring will be brown. Choice B is the correct answer.

This question asks you to analyze the results of a Punnett square. The best way to answer this question is to create the Punnett square and review the results before considering all of the choices. Determine the probabilities of each genotype and phenotype. Once you've done this, compare each choice to your results.

Sex-Linked Traits

Key Words...........

Sex-linked trait
Pedigree

A person who carries a recessive gene for a trait but does not exhibit the trait is called a carrier. For example, a female who has a gene for color blindness on one of her X chromosomes is not color-blind. Instead, she is a carrier for color blindness. That means that she may pass the gene for color blindness on to her children.

Some traits are **sex-linked traits**. This means that the genes for these traits are carried on sex chromosomes. Recall that sex chromosomes are the X and Y chromosomes that determine whether an organism is male or female. A female has two X chromosomes, whereas a male has an X chromosome and a Y chromosome.

Most sex-linked traits are recessive. If a trait is a recessive sex-linked trait, it usually appears only in males. The reason is that if the gene for the trait is located on the X chromosome that a male receives from his mother, he does not have another X chromosome to compensate for it. If the gene for the trait is located on one of the X chromosomes that a female receives, she has another X chromosome that may carry a dominant allele for the trait.

Color blindness is an example of a recessive trait that is linked to the X chromosome. A person who is color-blind cannot distinguish between certain colors, most commonly red and green. A female who has two X chromosomes must receive two alleles for color blindness in order to display the trait. A male, who has only one X chromosome, will be color-blind if he receives one allele for the trait.

Scientists often study the transmission of traits from one generation to the next by using a pedigree. A **pedigree** is a family record that shows which members inherit a specific trait over several generations. This pedigree shows how color blindness has been inherited in one family. Pay attention to the diagram's key to determine the meaning of each symbol.

EXAMPLE QUESTION

Hemophilia is a condition in which the blood cannot clot properly. Hemophilia is caused by a recessive allele carried on the X chromosome. Suppose a mother who carries the hemophilia gene on one of her X chromosomes has children with a man who exhibits hemophilia. Which of the following situations would you expect?

A   All of their daughters will exhibit hemophilia.

B   All of their sons will exhibit hemophilia.

C   All of their daughters will carry or exhibit hemophilia.

D   All of their sons will carry hemophilia.

DISCUSSION

Choice C is the correct answer. The daughters of this couple will receive an X chromosome from their father that contains the hemophilia gene. They will also receive an X chromosome from their mother. If they receive the X chromosome with the hemophilia gene, they will exhibit the condition. If not, they will carry it.

The sons will receive a Y chromosome from their father and an X chromosome from their mother. If they receive the X chromosome with the hemophilia gene, they will exhibit the condition. If not, they will neither exhibit the condition nor carry it.

LESSON

19

The Structure of DNA

Key Words...........

Nucleotide
Replication

For the last several lessons, you have been reading about traits and how they are inherited. The actual process of heredity is controlled by DNA. The information in DNA acts like a blueprint, directing how proteins will be assembled. It is the proteins that then regulate the cell's activities.

DNA is made up of individual nucleotides. A **nucleotide** consists of a phosphate, a sugar, and a base. Each nucleotide in DNA consists of four different nitrogen bases—adenine (A), thymine (T), guanine (G), and cytosine (C).

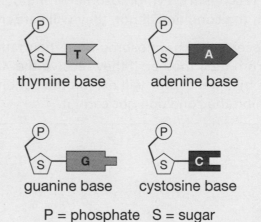

thymine base   adenine base

guanine base   cystosine base

P = phosphate   S = sugar

The nucleotides form long chains. Two chains twisted like a spiral staircase make up a molecule of DNA. Only certain bases can pair together to form the molecule. Adenine pairs with thymine, and cytosine pairs with guanine. One strand of the DNA molecule is said to be complementary to the other.

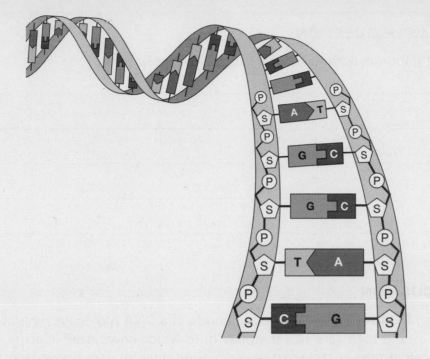

The process of copying DNA during cell division is called **replication**. During DNA replication, the strands of DNA separate from one another. Each strand acts as a template for a new strand to form. Once replication is complete, two new exact copies of the original DNA molecule are produced.

New strands

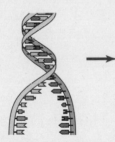 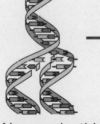 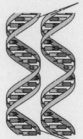

The strands separate. New nucleotides bond to each strand. Two DNA molecules are formed. Old strands

TEST TAKING STRATEGY

When a question asks you to summarize a process, be sure to go through the process step-by-step. Read through your answer to make sure you have included a description of what happens during the process and what the final result is.

EXAMPLE QUESTION

What happens during the process of DNA replication?

_____

_____

_____

_____

_____

DISCUSSION

During DNA replication, the two strands of a DNA molecule separate. Each strand then acts as a template onto which new bases attach. Once all of the separated bases are paired up with new bases, two new molecules of DNA are produced. If no errors occurred during replication, each molecule will be identical to the original.

LESSON 20

Protein Synthesis

The information in DNA is used to make proteins. Recall that traits, such as hair and eye color, are determined by proteins. Proteins are chains of amino acids. There are twenty different amino acids. The combination and arrangement of amino acids determine a protein's form and purpose.

Proteins are assembled on ribosomes, which are in the cytoplasm of a cell. DNA, however, does not leave the nucleus. The cell needs some way to get the information from DNA in the nucleus to the ribosomes in the cytoplasm. The nucleic acid RNA is used for this purpose. RNA carries information from DNA to the ribosomes and carries out the process by which proteins are made.

RNA is similar to DNA, but it has several important differences. For example, RNA consists of a single strand rather than a double strand of nucleotides. In addition, RNA has a uracil (U) base rather than thymine. RNA nucleotides contain the five-carbon sugar ribose rather than deoxyribose, as is found in DNA nucleotides. A cell contains many types of RNA. There are three main types of RNA: mRNA, tRNA, and rRNA.

Instructions in DNA are in the form of a code that depends on the arrangement of nucleotide bases. The nucleotides are read in triplets, or groups of three. There are 64 possible code words. The code words for making the protein are passed on from the DNA to an RNA molecule during the process known as **transcription**. During transcription, a molecule of DNA is copied into a complementary strand of RNA.

As you learned in the previous lesson, DNA consists of two long chains of bases organized as a double helix. To begin protein synthesis, the two strands of DNA separate. Complementary nucleotides of RNA are added to the strand, much like the process that occurs during DNA replication. However, in this case, the new strand is made of RNA instead of DNA. Many identical RNA molecules can be made from a single gene.

Key Words...........

Transcription
Messenger RNA
Codon
Translation
Transfer RNA
Ribosomal RNA
Protein synthesis

In prokaryotic cells, transcription occurs in the cytoplasm. In eukaryotic cells, it occurs in the nucleus. In both types of cells, translation occurs in the cytoplasm.

Some questions, such as this one, ask you to infer the meaning of a term. You have encountered this term in science. If you can't recall its meaning, try to figure out how the word is used outside of science. This may help you to answer the question.

The type of RNA that carries the instructions from DNA in a gene to where they will be translated is known as **messenger RNA** (mRNA). The instructions in mRNA are arranged as sequences of three nucleotides known as **codons**. Each codon on the mRNA strand codes for a particular amino acid, or it marks the beginning or end of a process.

Once the mRNA carries the information into the cytoplasm, a process known as translation begins. During **translation**, the information is decoded and used to arrange amino acids. In other words, the information is translated from nucleotides to amino acids. Translation involves the other two types of RNA. **Transfer RNA** (tRNA) carries amino acids to the ribosomes, where they are joined together to form proteins. **Ribosomal RNA** (rRNA) is part of the structure of ribosomes. The entire process of constructing proteins is known as **protein synthesis**.

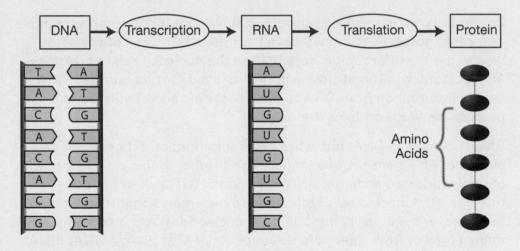

EXAMPLE QUESTION

Which is the best meaning for the term translation?

A   joining together

B   writing out

C   changing from one language to another

D   erasing

DISCUSSION

During the process of translation, information stored in the sequence of nucleotides is converted into a sequence of amino acids. This is most like changing from one language to another, which is choice C.

LESSON 21

Changes to Genetic Information

Although they are relatively rare, errors sometimes occur in the process of passing along genetic information. One type of error occurs when the DNA of an organism experiences a change. A change in the nucleotide sequence is called a **mutation**.

Cells have enzymes that act like proofreaders that check the sequence of nucleotides and make repairs as necessary. As a result, the number of mutations that occur during replication is usually small. Some mutations do occur naturally, however. In addition, DNA can be damaged by external factors such as ultraviolet radiation and exposure to certain chemicals.

Because DNA codes for the production of proteins, changes in DNA will change the resulting proteins. Some mutations have little or no affect on the organism. In rare cases, the mutation can have a beneficial affect on the organism by giving the organism some trait that makes it better enabled to survive in its environment. Still other mutations cause adverse affects on the organism, causing illness or even death.

In organisms that reproduce asexually, all mutations are passed directly onto the offspring. In organisms that reproduce sexually, mutations are divided into two categories. Mutations that occur in an organism's body cells are called **somatic mutations**. These mutations are passed along to any cells that result from the division of these cells but are not passed along to offspring. Mutations that occur in reproductive cells, gametes, are called **germinal mutations**. These mutations are passed on to offspring.

Key Words...........

Mutation
Somatic mutation
Germinal mutation

There are different types of mutations. An insertion mutation occurs when DNA segments are inserted in locations where they do not belong. A deletion mutation occurs when bits of DNA are deleted from where they belong. A substitution mutation occurs when one or more bases are substituted at particular locations.

If you cannot answer right away, place a mark in the margin beside the question. Then go on to the next question. Sometimes, one question will remind you of the information you need to answer another. Be sure, however, to go back and choose an answer for any questions you skipped.

Each of the 46 chromosomes in a human cell contains thousands of genes. A human cannot survive if it is missing even one of its 46 chromosomes.

Another type of change in an organism's genetic material occurs when abnormal numbers of chromosomes exist. Recall that when gametes—sperm and egg cells—form, pairs of homologous chromosomes separate. This process is known as disjunction.

In some cases, one or more pairs of chromosomes do not separate properly. As a result, one gamete receives both chromosomes and the other does not receive any. This process is called nondisjunction. If a gamete containing the chromosomes that did not separate becomes fertilized, the resulting offspring will have three copies of that chromosome instead of the normal two.

Because the genes on chromosomes determine how a person's body develops and functions, an abnormal number of chromosomes prevents the body from developing properly. Nondisjunction involving chromosome 21, for example, results in a condition known as Down syndrome. People with Down syndrome are characterized by a short stature, a rounded face with upper eyelids that cover the inner corners of the eyes, and some degree of mental retardation.

EXAMPLE QUESTION

A mutation occurs in the production of a reproductive cell. As a result of the mutation, the offspring fail to survive long enough to reproduce their own offspring. Which combination of terms best describes this mutation?

A somatic and neutral

B germinal and harmful

C somatic and beneficial

D germinal and neutral

DISCUSSION

The mutation affected a reproductive cell (gamete), so it is a germinal rather than a somatic change. Because the mutation made it impossible for the offspring to pass on their genetic information, the mutation was harmful. The correct answer is choice B.

LESSON 22

Genetic Technology

In 1973, two scientists named Stanley Cohen and Herbert Boyer revolutionized the study of genetics. They removed a gene that coded for rRNA from the DNA of an African clawed frog. They then inserted the gene into the DNA of *E. coli* bacteria. When transcription occurred in the bacteria, the frog rRNA was produced. This process of controlling genes for practical purposes became known as **genetic engineering** or **gene splicing**. The DNA made from two or more different organisms became known as **recombinant DNA**.

The actual process depends on the specific genetic engineering experiment, but the basic process is summarized in the diagram. The example shown here reviews the steps involved with transferring the human gene for insulin into bacteria. The process begins when DNA from both organisms is cut. Scientists cut DNA with bacterial enzymes called restriction enzymes. These enzymes bind to certain sequences of DNA and cut between specific nucleotides.

A vector is used to carry the gene into the desired cell. Common vectors include yeast and plasmids. In this example, the vector is a plasmid, which is a circular molecule of DNA. The DNA fragment from the human DNA is combined with that of the plasmid. The bacterial cells are then treated so they can take in the recombinant DNA.

Key Words..........
Genetic engineering
Gene splicing
Recombinant DNA
Cloning

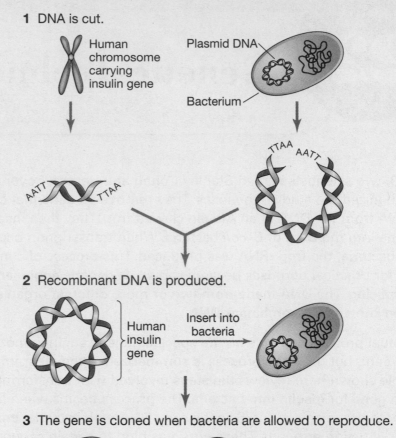

1 DNA is cut.

Human chromosome carrying insulin gene

Plasmid DNA

Bacterium

AATT TTAA

TTAA AATT

2 Recombinant DNA is produced.

Human insulin gene

Insert into bacteria

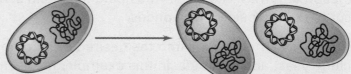

3 The gene is cloned when bacteria are allowed to reproduce.

Bacteria reproduce by binary fission. Recall from Lesson 7 that this is a type of asexual reproduction. As a result, the offspring produced are genetically identical to the parent cell. So when this bacterial cell reproduces, it also reproduces its plasmid DNA. The process through which the bacterial cell makes exact copies of the insulin gene is known as **cloning**.

Why would scientists want to insert a gene from one organism into another? One reason is to produce medicines or vaccines. In the example just discussed, insulin is a protein hormone that controls how the body processes sugar. People who have diabetes cannot produce enough insulin, so they must take injections of insulin. Insulin was taken from the pancreases of slaughtered cows and pigs. This process was slow and costly. Today, genetic engineering makes it possible to use bacteria to produce human insulin.

The processes of genetic technology are also used in agriculture. Scientists can add human genes to the genes of farm animals in order to produce human proteins. This is useful for proteins that cannot be produced through genetic engineering of bacteria. The human proteins are then extracted from the animals' milk.

Scientists also use cloning to produce identical animals. In early experiments, the nucleus of a cell from an embryo was inserted into an egg whose nucleus had been removed. The egg was then placed into a substitute mother and allowed to develop. In the late 1990s, however, a scientist successfully cloned a sheep using a cell that was not an embryonic cell. Producing identical organisms through cloning has many possible applications. However, it also poses opportunities for misuse.

EXAMPLE QUESTION

Which would be a reason why scientists would genetically engineer bacteria to produce human insulin?

A   Bacteria do not have their own genetic material.

B   Bacteria are living.

C   Bacteria are very small.

D   Bacteria reproduce quickly.

DISCUSSION

Bacteria are useful because they make many identical copies in a short amount of time. This enables scientists to produce more human insulin than would be obtained otherwise. Choice D is the correct answer.

Review

1 A Labrador retriever can be black, yellow, or brown. Which of these processes makes it possible for two Labradors to produce offspring of different colors?

A meiosis

B mitosis

C osmosis

D binary fission

2 Albinism is a genetic disorder in which the body is unable to produce the protein necessary for the production of melanin. Melanin is a pigment that gives dark colors to hair, skin, and eyes. According to this pedigree, what type of trait is albinism?

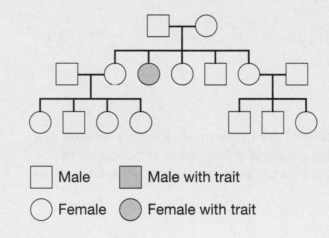

☐ Male ◼ Male with trait

◯ Female ⬤ Female with trait

F dominant

G recessive

H sex-linked

J acquired

3 The allele for tall height (T) is dominant over the allele for short height (t) in pea plants. One homozygous tall plant and one homozygous short plant are crossed. What are the genotype and phenotype of the offspring?

A TT; tall

B Tt; short

C Tt; tall

D tt; short

4 Cystic fibrosis is a genetic disorder caused by a recessive allele. Suppose two carriers for cystic fibrosis have a child together. What is the probability that the child will exhibit cystic fibrosis?

F 10%

G 25%

H 50%

J 100%

5 A strand of DNA consists of the following bases: ATT GCA CTG. What are the bases on the complementary strand of DNA?

A ATT GCA CTG

B TAA CGT GAC

C GTC ACG TTA

D UAA CGU GAC

6 A strand of DNA with sequence A-C-T-T-G serves as a template to form a corresponding sequence with a T-G-A-A-C pattern. During which process would this activity occur?

F replication

G transcription

H translation

J protein synthesis

7 This diagram shows the base sequence of a strand of DNA. From top to bottom, what sequence of mRNA would be created during transcription?

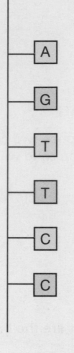

A AGTTCC

B UCAAGG

C CCTTFA

D TCAAGG

8 A mutation has occurred in an organism's cell. When the organism reproduces, the mutation does not appear in the offspring's genetic material. How can this be true?

F The mutation caused damage and was therefore not passed along to the next generation.

G The mutation was a change that did not cause harm to the organism.

H The mutation occurred in a sperm cell.

J The mutation did not occur in a gamete.

9 How is a gene from one organism combined with genes of another organism in genetic engineering?

Write your answer in your Answer Book.

_____

_____

_____

_____

10 An organism is cloned from another organism. Which statement about the cloned organism is true?

A   It is an improved version of the parent.

B   It contains genes from the parent along with genes from another organism.

C   It is identical to the parent in every way.

D   It lacks genetic material.

NOTICE: Photocopying any part of this book is forbidden by law.

95

Organisms and Ecosystems

Natural Selection

Key Words...........

Species
Variation
Inheritable
characteristic
Natural selection
Adaptation
Extinction

Some variations among organisms arise from new combinations of genes. Others result from germinal mutations.

You would not expect to find a polar bear living in Maryland. Nor would you look for a fish that is native to the shores of Maryland in the icy waters of the Antarctic. Organisms thrive in the environments for which they are best suited.

That does not mean that all organisms of the same type are equally suited to the same characteristics of their environment. With the exception of identical twins, members of a species produced as a result of sexual reproduction are genetically unique. A **species** is a group of organisms that can interbreed to produce fertile offspring.

Although the members of a species share many similar characteristics, there will be **variation** (differences) among the members. For example, all dogs are members of the same species. However, individual dogs differ from one another in terms of size, shape, color, agility, temperament, and so on. Some dogs, such as Labrador retrievers, have webbed feet that make them excellent swimmers. Other dogs, such as dachshunds, have short legs that make them able to move through tight spaces.

Great Dane   Afghan Hound   Dachshund

If an organism's variation gives it an advantage over other organisms in its environment, it will be more likely to survive and reproduce. If the variation is an **inheritable characteristic**, it will then be passed on to any offspring of the organism. The process in which organisms best suited to their environment as a result of favorable characteristics survive and reproduce is known as **natural selection**.

The theory of natural selection was first proposed by Charles Darwin in the 19th century. His conclusions were based on his observations of finch species on the Galapagos Islands. The finches had beaks of different size and shape depending on the types of food available where they lived. Scientists think that the finches evolved from a single species that first lived on the islands.

The small tree finch eats insects.

The vegetarian finch eats fruit and seeds.

The cactus finch eats cactus fruits and insects inside cactus flowers.

The development of a new species is known as speciation. This process can lead to greater biodiversity. Biodiversity is a measure of the number of different kinds of species on Earth.

Darwin's theory included the following ideas:

- Most organisms produce more offspring than are able to survive.

- This results in competition for resources, such as food and living space.

- Although the offspring are similar, some will have variations that make them better able to survive. Those that are unsuccessful at competition die out. Those with the favorable variations reproduce and pass the favorable variation on to their offspring.

- Over time, favorable variations are found in more and more offspring. A trait that improves an organism's chance for survival and reproduction is called an **adaptation**. A new species may develop, or evolve, in this way.

Organisms try to survive in their environments through adaptation. Despite this effort, many species become extinct. Extinction means the end of a species. **Extinction** sometimes occurs when environmental changes occur too quickly and organisms are unable to adapt fast enough to survive. This might happen in the case of a flood or volcanic eruption. It is estimated that more than 99 percent of the species that have ever lived on Earth have become extinct.

Be alert for multiple ideas or concepts within the same answer choice. All parts of a statement must be correct for it to be true. If any part of the statement is untrue, it must be an incorrect answer.

An organism's survival depends on how it adapts to a local environment. Useful traits in one place, such as a thick coat of fur in cold climates, could be useless or even harmful in another.

EXAMPLE QUESTION

Some insect species have developed an ability to resist pesticides. Which statement best describes this phenomenon?

A Because their survival depended on it, the insects developed variations that made them resistant to poisons.

B Natural selection results in an unfavorable variation for the insects.

C Random variation in the population led to a species with a favorable adaptation.

D Some of the insects became instantly immune when the poisons were introduced into their environment.

DISCUSSION

Random variation allows the organisms that are best suited to the conditions to survive. These variations are then passed down to their offspring. Eventually, these adaptations can lead to the formation of a new species. Choice C is the correct answer.

LESSON 24

Evidence of Change

The process of change over time is known as **evolution**. Since living things first appeared on Earth, species have appeared, changed, and disappeared. Evolution describes how species change over many generations as genetic information is passed on from parent to offspring. It also attempts to explain how species relate to each other. Evidence of evolution comes from many sources, including observation, the fossil record, anatomical similarities, and genetic information.

Observation   Many species produce numerous generations within a few years. This makes it possible to observe physical traits in successive generations. Recall that Darwin observed changes in the beak size and shape of finches and concluded that the finches adapted to changes in the size, shape, and hardness of the available food.

Organisms can be classified into different groups according to observations of their similarities and differences. A five-kingdom system of classification is commonly used today. **Kingdoms** are large, broad categories that group living things by the structure of their cells. Recall from Lesson 5 that there are two general types of cells: prokaryotes and eukaryotes. A prokaryote is a cell that lacks a membrane-bound nucleus or organelles. A eukaryote is a cell that contains a nucleus and membrane-bound organelles. Prokaryotes are limited to one of the five kingdoms—the Moneran Kingdom.

Key Words..........

Evolution
Kingdom
Fossil
Homologous structures
DNA fingerprint

Kingdom	Cells	Characteristics	Organisms
Moneran	Single	Cells have no nucleus	Bacteria
Protist	Single or multi	Cells have nucleus	Some algae, protozoa
Fungi	Single or multi	Cells have a wall and nucleus, but no chloroplasts	Yeast, mushrooms
Plants	Multi	Cells have a wall, nucleus, and chloroplasts	Some algae, moss, ferns, trees, flowering plants
Animals	Multi	Cells have a nucleus, but no wall or chloroplasts	Sponges, worms, insects, mammals, fish, amphibians, reptiles, birds

Fossil record   A **fossil** is the preserved remains of an organism that lived many years ago. Fossil evidence shows the changes between species that lived in the past and those alive today. As a result, scientists have often been able to use fossils to reconstruct the relationship or evolutionary link between extinct species and their modern relatives.

Anatomical similarities   Many species have a common physical, or anatomical, structure. For example, the human arm, whale flipper, horse leg, and bird wing all have the same bone shape. This suggests that they evolved from a common ancestor. Similar structures that began from a common ancestor are called **homologous structures**.

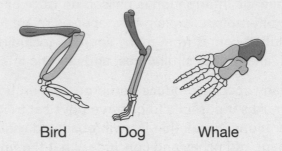

Bird   Dog   Whale

Genetic information   Organisms that look similar today are believed to have a more recent common ancestor than organisms that look very different. This applies to their genetic information as well. By comparing the sequences of amino acids of specific molecules, scientists can analyze evolutionary relationships among organisms.

For example, many organisms contain a red-blood-cell protein called hemoglobin. The amino acid sequence for this protein in humans is almost identical to the sequence for this protein in gorillas. They differ by only one amino acid. The human sequence, however, differs by 67 amino acids from the amino sequence in frogs. The more similar the sequences of amino acids, the shorter the length of time since the organisms shared a common ancestor. So humans and gorillas shared a common ancestor more recently than humans and frogs.

Scientists can compare the DNA of different organisms using a process known as gel electrophoresis. Recall from Lesson 22 that DNA can be cut into fragments using restriction enzymes. These fragments can be placed into a gel. An electric charge is then transferred to the gel.

When two charges of the same type are brought together, they repel one another. So, the DNA fragments, which are negatively charged, are repelled by the negative electrode. Charges that are different attract one another. So the DNA fragments are attracted to the positive electrode. Through this process, the DNA fragments are separated according to size. The pattern that is produced is known as a **DNA fingerprint**. The more similar the DNA fingerprints of two organisms, the more recently they shared a common ancestor.

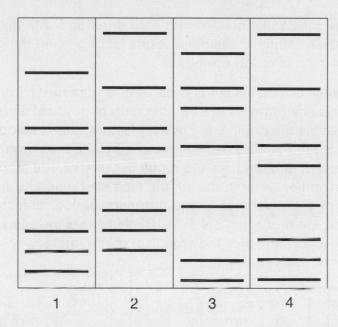

1   2   3   4

EXAMPLE QUESTION

What does the fossil record show about the history of species on Earth?

A   Species stay the same over time.

B   Species evolve from one form to another.

C   Modern species have no relationship to ancient species.

D   No new species have emerged in the last 200 million years.

DISCUSSION

The fossil record, and other evidence, shows that species constantly change over time. New species emerge from other species, and some species become extinct. Choice B is the correct answer.

NOTICE: Photocopying any part of this book is forbidden by law.

103

LESSON 25

Characteristics of an Ecosystem

Key Words..........

Ecology

Abiotic factor

Biotic factor

Ecosystem

Living things constantly interact with each other and with their environment. The study of the interactions among living things and their environment is called **ecology**.

Scientists called ecologists study organisms and their environments. An organism's environment is a combination of physical and biological factors that affect the organism. Physical factors, called **abiotic factors**, are those that are not alive. Abiotic factors include the amount of light the area receives, the temperature range in the area, the amount of precipitation and/or water in the air, the type of soil and its acidity, and the amount of available oxygen and nutrients. Biological factors, called **biotic factors**, are those that are alive. Biotic factors include all of the living organisms with which the organism might interact.

Environment

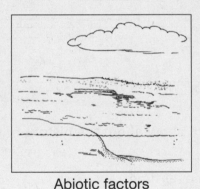
Abiotic factors

Biotic factors

Ecologists classify environments according to ecosystems. An **ecosystem** describes a collection of organisms and their relationships with the biotic and abiotic factors that affect their lives. A coral reef in the Caribbean and an Amazon rain forest are both examples of ecosystems.

EXAMPLE QUESTION

Which of the following is a biotic factor in an ecosystem?

A high temperature

B low humidity

C ground-covering mosses

D abundant water supply

DISCUSSION

A biotic factor is a living factor in an ecosystem. Choice C is correct because mosses are living organisms. Temperature, humidity, and water are abiotic, or nonliving, factors in an ecosystem.

This question asks you for an example of a biotic factor. Before looking at the choices, think about the definition of a biotic factor. Then look for a choice that fits the definition.

LESSON 26

Relationships Among Organisms

Key Words..........

Symbiosis
Mutualism
Commensalism
Parasitism
Parasite
Host
Predator
Prey

You interact with other humans everyday. You also interact with other animals and plants. In fact, all organisms interact with other organisms from the same species and with other species. Interactions among organisms can be classified as symbiosis or predation. **Symbiosis** is a permanent relationship between two different organisms. There are three different types of symbiosis.

Mutualism In this type of relationship, both organisms benefit from one another. For example, sea anemone and clownfish have a mutualistic relationship. The fish is protected by the sea anemone, and in return the sea anemone receives scraps of food from the fish. In addition, the clownfish lures larger fish into the anemone's tentacles.

Commensalism In this type of relationship, one organisms benefits from the other. The other organism is neither helped nor harmed by the relationship. For example, pilotfish, also known as remora, have a relationship with sharks. The pilotfish eat scraps of food left by the shark. The shark is not affected by the presence of the pilotfish.

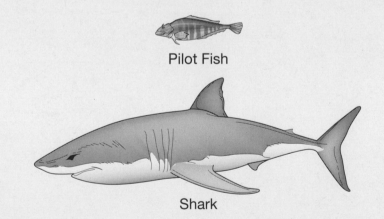

Pilot Fish

Shark

Parasitism In this type of relationship, one organism benefits and the other is harmed. The organism that benefits is called the **parasite**, and the other is called the **host**. Tapeworms and liver flukes are parasites that live in the bodies of other organisms. They feed off the host and often cause disease.

In predation, an animal known as a **predator** feeds on another animal. The animal that is killed and eaten is called the **prey**. Although it might seem unfortunate, predators play an important role in controlling the prey population. There are always many more individuals in the prey species to support a fewer number of predators. For example, a small pride of lions will feed upon a large populations of zebras.

Read a multiple-choice question and try to answer it without reading the answer choices. Focus on finding the answer yourself. This process will increase your concentration and help you read the question more clearly.

EXAMPLE QUESTION

Some species of shark allow small fish to enter their mouths without eating them. Inside the mouth, the small fish feed on debris around the teeth. The sharks get their teeth cleaned, which reduces the risk of decay and infection. Which term best categorizes this relationship?

A predation

B mutualism

C parasitism

D commensalisms

DISCUSSION

Both the sharks and the fish benefit from this relationship, so the correct answer is choice B, mutualism. Choice A is incorrect because the sharks do not feed on the fish. Choice C is incorrect because neither species suffers from the relationship, and choice D is incorrect because both species benefit from this relationship.

LESSON 27

Niches

Key Words...........
Niche
Producer
Consumer
Herbivore
Carnivore
Omnivore
Scavenger
Decomposer

A consumer that feeds directly on plants is usually called a primary consumer. A consumer that eats a primary consumer is called a secondary consumer, and so on. The final consumer in an ecosystem is often called the top consumer.

There are many different types of environments on Earth. And there are a great number of different types of organisms that live in each one. The many different types of organisms are often described as the diversity of life.

How can so many different types of organisms survive? As you have learned already, organisms are adapted to different environments, and they play specific roles in their environment. An organism's role in an environment is described as its **niche**.

As you learned in Unit II, the organisms that are capable of making food are known as **producers**. In most ecosystems, plants are the producers. This is their niche.

The organisms that eat producers to obtain food are known as **consumers**. Some consumers, called **herbivores**, eat only plants. Other consumers, known as **carnivores**, eat other animals. Many consumers are **omnivores**, which means that they eat both plants and animals.

Some organisms in an ecosystem "clean up" the remains left by other organisms. One such group of organisms includes scavengers. A **scavenger** is organism that feeds off other organisms that have already been killed or have died. A turkey vulture is an example of a scavenger.

Another group of organisms consists of decomposers. **Decomposers** are organisms that break down the remains of dead organisms. In the process, they return energy and nutrients to the ecosystem. Fungi and bacteria are decomposers in many ecosystems.

EXAMPLE QUESTION

The role of decomposers can best be likened to a

A trash collector

B recycler

C manufacturer

D bus

DISCUSSION

Choice B is the correct answer. Decomposers break down dead matter and return energy and nutrients to the ecosystem. As a result, they reuse or recycle materials.

TEST TAKING STRATEGY

This type of question involves an analogy. To answer this question, you have to find the relationship between two things that are otherwise dissimilar. In this case, think about the role of the organism. Ask yourself what it does in its environment. Then try to think of who does a similar role in a very different environment.

LESSON 28

Food Chains and Webs

An ecosystem can be divided into trophic levels. Each step in a food chain relates to a trophic level. Producers occupy the first trophic level.

Energy is constantly flowing through every ecosystem. The energy of sunlight is first trapped by producers during photosynthesis. That energy is then stored in the plant and obtained by consumers that eat the plant. A consumer uses some of the energy and stores some in its own body. If that consumer is then eaten, its stored energy is obtained by its consumer. As a result, energy flows from one organism to the next. A *food chain* describes the flow of energy from producers to consumers to decomposers. The diagram below shows an example of a food chain.

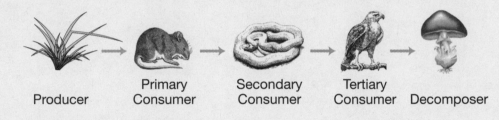

Producer   Primary   Secondary   Tertiary   Decomposer
                  Consumer   Consumer   Consumer

In actual ecosystems, producers and consumers belong to more than one food chain at the same time. Food chains are interconnected in what is known as a *food web*. A food web that exists on land is called a terrestrial food web. A food web that exists in the ocean is called an oceanic food web or marine food web.

EXAMPLE QUESTION

How might a terrestrial food web be affected if the lions were removed?

A The amount of grass would decrease because the zebra population would increase.

B The number of trees would increase because the carnivores would be removed.

C The cheetah population would decrease because there would be no more competition.

D The zebra population would decrease because zebras are herbivores.

DISCUSSION

Lions are carnivores that feed on other animals, such as zebras. If the lions are removed by poachers or other means, the zebra population will increase. Zebras are herbivores that feed on grasses and other plants. If the zebra population increases, it will feed on more grass. Choice A is the correct answer.

Not all of the energy stored in producers is passed along to decomposers. In fact, only about 10 percent of the energy from each trophic level is passed along to the next level. Some of the energy is used to carry on the life functions of the organism. An additional amount of energy dissipates as heat. A pyramid is often used to represent the energy in an ecosystem. The wide base shows that the greatest amount of energy is at the lowest trophic level.

LESSON 29

Ecological Succession

Key Words...........

Ecological succession

Climax community

Pioneer species

For many ecosystems, the organisms are in balance with the physical environment. Both energy and matter flow through the ecosystem in a relatively constant state. As a result, the ecosystem is said to be stable.

What happens, then, if something within the ecosystem is upset? For example, suppose a forest fire destroys most of the trees in a forest or a flood eliminates many animals' homes. In general, specific changes in a component of an ecosystem can have unpredictable effects on the entire system. However, the components tend to react in such a way that will restore the ecosystem to its original condition. Through a series of gradual changes, the same types of populations and communities will return to the ecosystem.

When one community is entirely replaced by another, the process is called **ecological succession**. The final community that results from ecological succession is known as the **climax community**. The climax community is diverse, stable, and lives in balance with the environment.

Consider the example of a pond or lake. Suppose soil is washed into a lake. The water fills up with solid materials. The populations of fish that live in deep water decrease, while the fish that live in shallow water increase in number. Plants that live along the lake die, decay, and add more solid material to the lake. Fish populations continue to dwindle. The lake gradually turns into a bog. Eventually, the area becomes dry land.

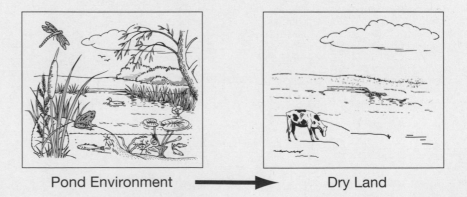

Pond Environment   ⟶   Dry Land

The animal populations in an ecosystem depend on the plant populations. For this reason, communities are often named according to their dominant plant types. The first group of plants to appear in a bare region is called a **pioneer species** or pioneer community. These are generally grasses or small flowering plants that make the ground more suitable to other species.

EXAMPLE QUESTION

An ecosystem experiences a volcanic eruption. At some point, a climax community is established. What is the nature of this community?

A   It is the first community of plants to establish itself in the region.

B   It is the stable community formed at the end of its succession.

C   It is the community of organisms destroyed by the lava.

D   It is a temporary community formed as the ecosystem recovers from the damage.

DISCUSSION

Choice B is the correct answer. The climax community is a stable community formed at the end of the succession. It is a diverse, mature community that is in balance with the components of the ecosystem.

LESSON
30

Changes to Ecosystems

Key Words...........

Population
Limiting factor
Resource depletion
Urbanization

The largest population that a given environment can support over a long period of time is known as the carrying capacity. As conditions in the environment change, the carrying capacity might change as well.

Throughout this unit you have learned about organisms and how they interact with each other and their ecosystems. In the previous lesson, you discovered how organisms and ecosystems respond to the destruction of ecosystems through ecological succession. In this lesson, you will consider how populations of organisms are affected by changes—both natural and man-made.

You often encounter the term *population*. In science, the definition of a **population** is all of the members of the same species that inhabit a specific area. All of the field mice in a meadow, for example, make up a population.

The size of a population can change over time. Most populations eventually stabilize rather than grow endlessly. The reason is that as a population grows, it puts more demands on the resources of its ecosystem. For example, a larger population of lions in a particular savanna requires more food than a smaller population does. If enough food is not available to feed a larger population, some lions will die. As a result, the size of the population decreases. The size of the lion population is thus limited by the availability of food.

Environmental factors that limit the size of a population are called **limiting factors**. In addition to the availability of food, other limiting factors include the availability of water, oxygen, and sunlight, as well as the relationships with other organisms and the ability to remove wastes.

Humans are unique in that they can change their environment to change the natural production of resources. Humans can plant farms to grow food, construct buildings for shelter, develop vitamins for nutrients, and so on. When humans change the natural supply of resources and change the limits of the population, they change the flow of energy through the environment. In the process, they place the environment at risk, stressing its ability to support life.

Much of the stress humans place on the environment results from the growth of the human population. The size of the human population remained relatively stable for many years. Then, at the time of the Industrial Revolution, the human population began to grow significantly. The growth of the human population is shown in the graph below.

Human Population	Year
1 billion	1804
2 billion	1927
3 billion	1960
4 billion	1974
5 billion	1987
6 billion	1999
Projected	
7 billion	2011 – 2015
8 billion	2026 – 2028

Another factor that will affect the dynamics of a population is the presence of a disease. Diseases are especially dangerous to populations in which the organisms are genetically identical or similar. All of the organisms can be wiped out by the disease. If, however, some of the organisms have a genetic makeup that enables them to survive the disease, they will be able to stay alive and reproduce.

As the population grows, people require more and more resources. Natural resources, such as soil, water, and air, are being used at faster rates than they can be recycled in nature. In addition, energy requirements expand with the population. Limited energy resources can run out in the foreseeable future. The overuse of natural resources is known as **resource depletion**.

In addition, the more people on Earth, the more waste they produce. As a result, all types of pollution increase. The air is polluted when dangerous gases are released through the combustion of fuels, for example. Also, Earth has a natural energy balance made possible by greenhouse gases in the atmosphere. If humans release additional greenhouse gases, too much heat will be trapped near Earth's surface. Over time, global temperatures may rise, causing polar ice caps to melt and ecosystems to change. Water and soil are polluted when solid wastes, oil spills, and chemicals such as insecticides are used and disposed of.

Another way that humans harm natural ecosystems is by physically altering the ecosystem. Through the process of **urbanization**, human populations clear land or change water patterns to make way for buildings and roadways. The organisms that lived in that ecosystem are forced to relocate. If they cannot move, they will die. For example, Maryland is in danger of losing several fish species. Removing water from their ecosystems for drinking and irrigation are major threats against these species.

EXAMPLE QUESTION

In some regions of the world, rainforests are being destroyed to clear land for homes and farms. How does this practice place Earth's environment at risk?

____

____

____

____

____

DISCUSSION

The trees in rainforests carry out photosynthesis. This means that they remove carbon dioxide from the atmosphere and provide oxygen. As these trees are removed, the natural balance of gases in the atmosphere is upset. The increased carbon dioxide can lead to global warming as well as a decrease in breathable air.

TEST TAKING STRATEGY

Some questions have more than one part. Read each question carefully to make sure you know exactly what is being asked. Then check your answer to see that you have answered every part of the question.

NOTICE: Photocopying any part of this book is forbidden by law.

Review

1   According to the theory of natural selection, strains of bacteria become resistant to antibiotics because

   A   the bacteria do not require energy to survive
   B   some bacteria have an adaptation and survive
   C   bacteria never change in form
   D   bacteria must live within host organisms

2   Suppose that a short plant occupies a position in a forest close to the ground. The forest is not very dense with trees, but those that exist have created a thick covering of leaves and branches above the plant. Which adaptation would most likely help the plant to survive?

   F   shorter trunk
   G   wide, flat leaves
   H   thick roots
   J   thinner branches

3   Which of these organisms would be classified as a prokaryote?

   A   jellyfish
   B   mushroom
   C   moss
   D   bacteria

4   Which is an abiotic factor in a bird's environment?

   F   sunlight it receives
   G   tree in which it lives
   H   insects it eats
   J   leaves it eats

5 Birds called egrets feed on insects and lizards forced out of their hiding places by the movement of Cape buffalo in Tanzania. The buffalo are not affected in any way by the birds. What type of relationship do these animals exhibit?

    A commensalism

    B decomposition

    C mutualism

    D parasitism

6 A cow is a herbivore. Which of these foods would you expect a cow to eat?

    F mice

    G grass

    H mushrooms

    J steak

7 Which represents the most likely flow of energy through an ecosystem?

    A snake ⟶ mouse ⟶ grass ⟶ hawk

    B mouse ⟶ grass ⟶ hawk ⟶ snake

    C grass ⟶ mouse ⟶ snake ⟶ hawk

    D hawk ⟶ snake ⟶ mouse ⟶ grass

8 What is a food web and what are the types of organisms in a food web? How does a terrestrial food web differ from a marine food web?

Write your answer in your Answer Book.

_____

_____

_____

_____

_____

9 Which of the following most likely represents ecological succession on an abandoned farm?

F   grasses ⟶ clover ⟶ shrubs ⟶ maple trees

G   maple trees ⟶ shrubs ⟶ clover ⟶ grasses

H   shrubs ⟶ grasses ⟶ maple trees ⟶ clover

J   clover ⟶ maple trees ⟶ shrubs ⟶ grasses

10 Part of a forest is cut down to make room for a new housing community. How does this example of urbanization most directly affect the bird population living in the forest?

A   It causes an increase in their population because it provides them with new homes.

B   It causes an increase in their population because it destroys their predators.

C   It causes a decrease in their population because it destroys their habitat.

D   It causes a decrease in their population because it adds carnivores to their ecosystem.

The Scientific Process

LESSON

31

The Scientific Method

Key Words...........

Scientific method
Hypothesis
Data
Theory

Although the scientific method is often described as a series of steps, there is no single order in which the steps are completed. In fact, some steps are completed more than once. For example, a scientist might recognize early on that the hypothesis is unlikely. He or she may then go back and develop a new hypothesis and design a new investigation.

Have you ever wondered why something in the world happens as it does? For example, maybe you have asked why the sky is blue, why leaves change colors in autumn, or how fish breathe under water. Whenever you ask an answerable question about the natural world, you are acting like a scientist.

Asking a question is often the first step in a process known as the scientific method. The **scientific method** is the procedure a scientist follows to find answers to questions or solve problems. The scientific method is summarized in the diagram below.

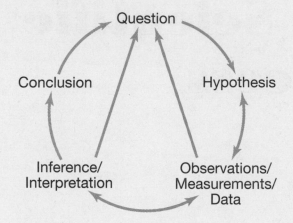

What do you do when you ask a question? Sometimes you come up with possible answers. A scientist does this as well. A possible answer to the question or an explanation for an event is called a **hypothesis**.

A scientist uses the hypothesis to make a prediction. A prediction is a statement about what the scientist expects to happen. A prediction is usually stated in an *if . . . then* fashion. For example, *if* the temperature of the culture is increased, *then* more organisms will grow.

The question addressed by the scientific method must be a specific type of question. It must be answerable by measurement or observation. For example, you cannot use the scientific method to answer opinion questions. In addition, science cannot answer questions that require some other form of inquiry, such as those involving religious and moral decisions.

When possible, scientists design experiments to test the hypothesis. When an experiment is not possible or practical, a scientist must make careful observations. In either case, the scientist records observations and measurements known as **data** during the investigation. The scientist later organizes the data in order to identify any trends in the information. At the end of the investigation, the scientist tries to use the data to draw a conclusion about whether the hypothesis was correct.

What happens if the hypothesis is not supported by the data? Whether or not the hypothesis is proven to be true, scientists learn from any scientific investigation. If the hypothesis is false, the scientist can propose a new hypothesis and test it in a new experiment. If the hypothesis is true, it may lead the scientist to new questions and new investigations or it may confirm previous results.

If many scientists repeat an investigation and reach the same conclusion, the hypothesis may become part of a theory. A **theory** is a broad explanation that ties together a range of observations and explanations about how processes are thought to occur.

Consider the following example to get an idea of how the scientific method can be used. For many years, from the time of Aristotle, people believed that living organisms came from nonliving objects. There were many observations that led them to this conclusion. For example,

> *Before the invention of refrigerators, meat would rot quickly because it was left out in the heat. As it rotted, flies would appear all over it. People concluded that rotting meat produced flies.*

Instead of accepting these conclusions, a scientist would ask a question:

> *Does rotting meat produce flies?*

The scientist would also propose a hypothesis:

> *Only flies can produce more flies. Rotting meat does not produce flies.*

Based on the hypothesis, the scientist can make a prediction:

> *If rotting meat does not produce flies, then there will be no flies on rotting meat in a sealed container.*

In everyday language, the term *theory* is used more loosely than in science. When people say they have a theory about something, they are more often describing a feeling or a hunch. In science, a theory is an explanation based on repeated observations. A scientific theory can be used to explain events and to predict future events.

Before you read through the answer choices for a question such as this one, carefully identify the details of the question. Be careful, because all of the choices could be testable hypotheses. Only one, however, relates to the observation described.

The next step is to test the hypothesis. Several experiments have been used to test this particular hypothesis. They included different variations of placing meat in sealed containers that were not exposed to contaminants in the air. The control group would be the meat exposed to contaminants in the air, whereas the experimental group would consist of meat not exposed to contaminants in the air. The data showed that no flies appeared on the experimental group. The conclusion:

Only flies can make more flies.

The explanation, as it turned out, was that flies had laid eggs in the meat. Maggots hatched from the eggs and grew into adult flies. If the eggs are prevented from being laid, the flies will not appear.

EXAMPLE QUESTION

A scientist is studying a population of bacteria. He notices that when a culture of bacteria is placed near a heat source, the population flourishes and then eventually dies as the temperature continues to rise. He decides to investigate this phenomenon. What is a hypothesis that might result from the observation?

A Populations of bacteria can be quite large.

B Some bacteria can tolerate heat better than others.

C The bacteria grow best within a narrow temperature range.

D Bacteria need a constant supply of food in order to thrive.

DISCUSSION

The hypothesis must be a statement that is a proposed explanation for an observation. In this case, the observation is that the bacteria grow well as temperature increases up to a certain point. When the temperature becomes too high, the population cannot survive. A good hypothesis would relate the survival of the population to temperature. Choice C is the correct answer.

LESSON 32

Controlled Experiments

When you are attempting to answer a scientific question, you cannot simply state your opinion as a conclusion. Instead, you need to obtain data that can be verified by experimentation. As you learned in the previous lesson, scientists obtain data by conducting an experiment.

In an experiment, a scientist controls the factors that could affect the outcome. In this type of experiment, known as a controlled experiment, the scientist manipulates one variable and observes the results. A **variable** is a factor that might affect the outcome of the investigation.

A variable that is changed during the experiment is called a **manipulated variable**, and a variable that is observed as a result of the change is called a **dependent variable**. For example, suppose a scientist conducts a controlled experiment to find out how fertilizer affects the height of a plant. The manipulated variable in the experiment will be the amount or type of fertilizer used on the plants. The height of the plant as a result of changes in the fertilizer is the dependent variable.

Key Words...........

Variable
Manipulated variable
Dependent variable
Experimental group
Control group

--- Control Group
— Experimental Group

How will a scientist know that the dependent variable changed as a result of the manipulated variable? For example, it might simply be coincidence that a particular plant grew after receiving fertilizer. To avoid such a possibility, every good experiment should have two groups to be studied—the **experimental group** and the **control group**. The two groups should be identical except for the fact that the experimental group undergoes a change in its independent variable. Every other factor must stay the same.

In the case of the fertilizer experiment, the type of soil, the type of plant, the amount of sunlight, the temperature, and the amount of water are some of the factors that cannot change during the experiment. The group of plants for which the amount of fertilizer is changed is the experimental group. The remaining plants are the control group.

It may sometimes seem that experiments in a laboratory have nothing to do with the real world. This misconception could not be farther from the truth. Scientists work in laboratory conditions when possible because it enables them to control the conditions of the experiment. They can then apply what they learn to the real world. For example, a scientist might use a laboratory to determine how a chemical breaks down in the soil. This information then becomes essential to determining when, how, and if that chemical should be used outside the laboratory. That chemical may be used in pesticides on farms because it can protect crops without harming the environment.

EXAMPLE QUESTION

Ian wanted to find out if buttermilk makes a cake rise higher. He mixed two identical batches of cake matter using the same recipe. The only difference was that he put ordinary milk in one and buttermilk in the other. After baking equal amounts of batter at the same temperature and for the same period of time, Ian measured the height of the cakes. What was Ian's manipulated variable in this experiment?

A the type of milk

B the shape of the cakes

C the height of the cakes

D the recipe for the cakes

DISCUSSION

Ian has correctly identified and held constant many variables that might affect the outcome. The manipulated variable that he changed was the kind of milk in each cake. The dependent variable was the height of the cake. Choice A is the correct answer.

LESSON 33

Tools and Measurements

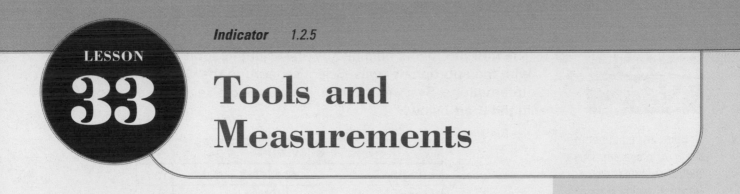

In an experiment, scientists use instruments or tools to make measurements and observations. Several useful tools are described in the diagram below.

A ruler measures length or distance.

A thermometer measures temperatures.

Graduated cylinders and beakers measure volume.

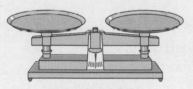

A pan balance measures mass.

A spring scale measures weight.

A stopwatch measures time.

Microscopes and hand lenses magnify small objects.

Telescopes and binoculars reveal the details of far-away objects.

Calculators and computers assist calculators, organize data, and make graphs.

SI units are a subset of the metric system. The metric system is an international system of measurement based on units of 10. The metric system is useful because it is designed to make conversions and calculations easier than with other systems of measurement. In 1960, an international conference streamlined the metric system by creating the International System of Units, which is built upon 7 metric units.

The measurements obtained by any scientific tools must be described with the appropriate units. Scientists around the world use the SI (International System of Units). It includes the seven base units listed in the chart below.

Base Units		
Length	Meter	m
Mass	Gram	g
Time	Second	s
Temperature	Degree Celsius	°C
Amount of Substance	Mole	mol
Electric Current	Ampere	A
Fluid Volume	Liter	L

Additional units can be derived by combining base units. Some common derived units are shown here.

Derived Units		
Density	Kilograms per cubic meter	kg/m^3
Speed	Meters per second	m/s
Force/Weight	Newton	$N\ (m \bullet kg/s^2)$
Solid Volume	Cubic centimeter	cm^3

EXAMPLE QUESTION

The density of an object equals its mass divided by its volume. Which choice lists the tools that could be used to find the density of a quartz crystal?

A   graduated cylinder and beaker

B   pan balance and stopwatch

C   spring scale and ruler

D   graduated cylinder and pan balance

DISCUSSION

To find density, you need to know the mass and the volume of the object. You can use a pan balance to find the mass and a graduated cylinder to find the volume. Choice D is the correct answer.

LESSON 34
Laboratory Safety

Laboratory safety is an important part of every investigation. Knowing how to use equipment properly will help prevent accidents or at least guide you in the event of an accident.

One of the most important guidelines for being safe in the laboratory is to follow directions in every detail and pay attention to any cautions from an instructor. Never substitute chemicals or lab equipment. If an accident should occur, tell your teacher or lab instructor immediately, before you do anything else.

The diagrams below illustrate some other important safety precautions.

No food or drink in the lab. Chemicals might contaminate it and make it poisonous.

Tie back or secure loose hair and clothing. Try to avoid wearing loose clothing on lab days.

Wear goggles when you work with chemicals or flames.

If chemicals get in or near your eyes, rinse them immediately and thoroughly with water. Tell your teacher.

Protect your hands with gloves or tongs when you touch hot containers.

Tilt test tubes away from you when they are being heated.

Never hold a test tube directly under your nose. If permitted, waft the vapors towards you. Never taste chemicals.

Several symbols identify precautions that should be taken during an investigation. They might also identify emergency stations and other locations around the lab.

This symbol indicates the presence of poisonous chemicals.

This symbol indicates the presence of flammable chemicals.

This symbol indicates the location of sharp objects.

This symbol indicates the location of the eyewash station.

This symbol indicates a shower or running water.

This symbol indicates the location of a fire alarm.

EXAMPLE QUESTION

List four safety precautions you should take when heating a chemical in a test tube over a flame.

_____

_____

_____

_____

DISCUSSION

Heating a test tube is a common step in an experiment. Remember these safety tips:

1. Put on goggles.
2. Tie back or secure loose hair and clothing.
3. Tilt the test tube away from you.
4. Use tongs and gloves to move the hot test tube.

LESSON

35

Organizing Data

Some investigations will produce a large amount of data. It will be difficult to analyze the data without organizing it in a useful way. Whenever you organize data, look for patterns. How are things alike or different? Is there a steady increase, decrease, or no change at all? What common features are there?

Tables, charts, graphs, and other visual models can be used to organize the data and make it easier to interpret.

Common Ways to Present Information	
Chart/Table	Summarizes data in rows and columns
Diagram/Model	Uses pictures to explain or show detail
Bar Graph	Uses bars to show the magnitude of the data
Line Graph	Uses a line to relate two sets of data or show how data change over time
Circle Graph	Divides a circle into wedges to show how parts relate to the whole
Flowchart	Series of boxes that show the order of steps or how different steps relate

Whenever creating a table or chart, follow these basic rules:

- Organize the data sequentially, or in numeric order.
- Include a title for the table or chart.
- Label the columns and include units for measurements.

Whenever creating a graph, follow these basic rules:

- Include a title or caption and other labels as needed.
- Choose an appropriate number scale, if necessary.
- For bar and line graphs, put the dependent variable on the horizontal axis, or x-axis, and the dependent variable on the vertical axis, or y-axis.

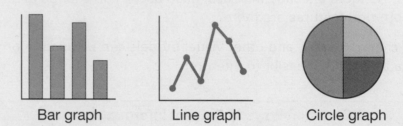

Bar graph   Line graph   Circle graph

Consider the following example to see how data might be presented. Dr. Trier measured and recorded the volume of a certain gas at different temperatures. The data can be organized into a table.

Temperature (°C)	Volume (L)
0	0.9
100	1.2
200	1.5
300	1.8
400	2.1
500	2.4

It can also be represented by a line graph.

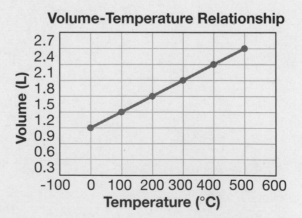

Volume-Temperature Relationship

EXAMPLE QUESTION

Suppose you studied the chemical composition of a sample of soil. What would be the *best* way to show your results?

A diagram

B chart

C circle graph

D flowchart

DISCUSSION

A circle graph would allow you to show the parts of a whole. Each part would be proportional to the percentage it represents. Choice C is the best answer.

TEST TAKING STRATEGY

The word *best* will appear in some questions. When you see this word, it should tell you that more than one answer choice might be correct. You are looking for the answer choice that is better than another.

LESSON 36

Using Mathematics

Key Words...........

Ratio
Proportion
Scientific notation

You read a ratio in such a way that you compare one number with the other. This ratio would be read as 15 is to 25 or 15 out of 25.

Mathematics is the language of science. Many relationships in nature can be analyzed and described using ratios, proportions, and equations. A **ratio** is a method of comparing numbers. For example, suppose the data from an experiment shows that 15 out of 25 offspring plants have purple flows. The numbers 15 and 25 form a ratio. You can write a ratio in three different ways:

$$15 \text{ to } 25; \qquad 15:25; \qquad \frac{15}{25}$$

You usually express a ratio in lowest terms.

$$\frac{15}{25} = \frac{3}{5}$$

Two equal ratios form a **proportion**. Proportions are often useful because their cross products are equal. A cross product is found by multiplying the numerator of one ratio by the denominator of the other.

$$\frac{a}{b} = \frac{c}{d}, \text{ so } a \times d = b \times c$$

You can use a proportion to find a missing value if you are trying to increase or decrease the amounts of materials used in an investigation.

In science, you will often encounter numbers that are very large or very small. For example, the speed of light in a vacuum is 300 000 000 meters per second. To make it easier to write and calculate these types of numbers, scientists use a shorthand notation known as **scientific notation**. In scientific notation, the numerical part of the number is written as a number between 1 and 10 multiplied by a power of 10.

To write the speed of light in scientific notation, move the decimal until you have a number between 1 and 10. Move the decimal point 8 places to the left. The number of places you move the decimal point is the power of 10. So the speed of light in meters per second is

$$300\ 000\ 000 = 3 \times 10^8$$

If you move the decimal to the right, the power of 10 is a negative number. The conversion below shows how to write the mass of an electron in scientific notation.

$$0.000\ 000\ 000\ 000\ 000\ 000\ 000\ 000\ 000\ 000\ 911 \text{ kilograms} =$$

$$9.11 \times 10^{-31}$$

Scientific notation is helpful when comparing the relative order of magnitude of two values. An order of magnitude is a number rounded to the nearest power of 10. For example, the height of a person is on the order of 10^0, or about 1 m. That does not mean that the average person is only 1 m tall, but the height is closer to 1 m than to 10 m. Similarly, the length of a bug might be on the order of 10^{-3} m. The ratio of the human height to the bug length is $10^0/10^{-3}$. When you simplify this ratio, you get 10^3, or 1000. This means that a person is 3 orders of magnitude taller than the bug, or 1000 times taller than the bug.

It is often important to judge the reasonableness of an answer. One way to do this is to estimate the answer. An estimate is a number close to the actual number but not exactly. By estimating what the answer will be, you can recognize if you made a mistake when entering information into your calculator or computer.

EXAMPLE QUESTION

The moon is roughly 384 000 000 m from Earth. How would you write this distance in scientific notation?

A 3.84×10^6

B 3.84×10^8

C 3.84×10^{-8}

D 3.84×10^{-6}

DISCUSSION

To find the answer, move the decimal point to the left until you reach the first digit. You must move the decimal point 8 places to reach the 3. This number becomes the exponent of 10. Because you moved to the left, the exponent is a positive number. So choice B is the correct answer.

LESSON 37

Identifying Relationships

Key Words...........
Precision
Accuracy

The results of an investigation might be precise but not accurate if there are sources of error in the procedure. It is important to review the procedure to identify any possible sources of error. For example, are you using the equipment correctly? Are you using the correct units with each measurement?

All around the world, numerous groups of researchers are presently at work trying to answer the same questions. One reason why different groups of researchers might work on the same question is because the different groups will approach the question in different ways. Another is because experimental data must be obtained from several investigators in order for the conclusions to be considered valid. It is not enough for a single group to reach a conclusion.

Once you establish that you have valid data, you must analyze the data to identify relationships between quantities. If you recognize a relationship, you can develop a mathematical model that describes the relationship.

As an example, consider early experiments conducted by Jacques Charles to investigate the relationship between the temperature and volume of a gas. The graph below is similar to that produced by Charles after investigating oxygen in a cylinder with a movable piston at different temperatures.

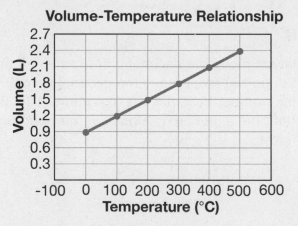

Charles was able to determine a trend in the data. Volume increases as temperature increases when pressure is held constant. The next step was to express this result as a mathematical equation. The resulting equation became known as Charles' Law:

$$V_1 T_1 = V_2 T_2$$

How reliable are the results of an investigation? Two methods of describing the reliability of results are precision and accuracy. A result has high **precision** if the same result is obtained after repeating the measurement several times. A measurement has high **accuracy** if it is close to the accepted value. A reliable measurement should be both precise and accurate.

A dartboard is often used to compare precision with accuracy. In A, the darts all strike the same region (high precision), but they are far from the bull's-eye (low accuracy). In B, the darts are spread apart (low precision), but they are closer to the bull's-eye (higher accuracy). In C, the darts are close together (high precision) and close to the bull's-eye (high accuracy).

TEST TAKING STRATEGY

Remember that some questions have more than one part. It is easy to complete one part of the answer and think you are finished. Get in the habit of rereading the question to make sure you have answered all parts before you move on.

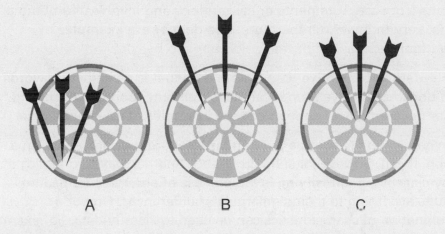

A   B   C

EXAMPLE QUESTION

The accepted value for the speed of light in a vacuum is 3.0×10^8 m/s. Suppose you are trying to measure the speed of light. How can your results be either precise or accurate, but not both?

_____

_____

_____

DISCUSSION

Your measurements can be precise but not accurate if you have the same results many times but the result is not close to the accepted value. If your setup causes you to reach an incorrect measurement, but you carefully conduct your measurement the same way each time, you will end up with a precise result. Your measurement can be accurate but not precise if your results are close to the accepted value but your measurements differ each time you conduct the investigation.

LESSON 38

Classification

Key Words...........

Quantitative data
Qualitative data
Classifying
Dichotomous key

Most of the data collected during an investigation will be disorganized. So far you have learned how to order and present mathematical data. Mathematical data is known as **quantitative data**. This is data that results from measurements or calculations and involves numbers and units. Length, mass, temperature, and density are examples of quantitative data.

Other data is **qualitative data**. This is data that is described in words and does not involve numerical measurements. Color, texture, and other descriptions of appearance are examples of qualitative data.

Qualitative data cannot be put in numerical order or presented on a graph. It can, however, still be organized. Another way to organize data is by classifying. **Classifying** is the process of arranging items into groups according to their similarities or differences. One or a combination of characteristics can be used to classify data. For example, living things are classified into groups according to such characteristics as the structure of their cells, whether or not they can conduct photosynthesis, and whether they are carnivores or herbivores.

You learned in Lesson 24 that living things are organized into large groups called kingdoms. The diagram below shows that kingdoms are further divided into more specific groups.

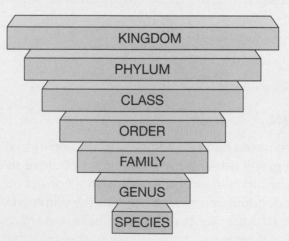

KINGDOM
PHYLUM
CLASS
ORDER
FAMILY
GENUS
SPECIES

Another type of classification system is called a **dichotomous key**. In this system, data is divided into two categories, such as yes and no. The table below uses only "yes" and "no" to classify organisms by their cell parts.

Organelle	Bacteria	Plants	Animals
Cell wall	Yes	Yes	No
Cell membrane	Yes	Yes	Yes
Nucleus	No	Yes	Yes
Ribosomes	Yes	Yes	Yes
Mitochondria	No	Yes	Yes
Chloroplasts	No	Yes	No

EXAMPLE QUESTION

The chart shows the classification of several animals.

	1	2	3	4
Kingdom	Animalia	Animalia	Animalia	Animalia
Phylum	Chordata	Chordata	Chordata	Chordata
Class	Mammalia	Mammalia	Mammalia	Mammalia
Order	Carnivora	Ungulate	Primates	Carnivora
Family	Canidae	Equidae	Pongidae	Canidae
Genus	*Canis*	*Equus*	*Pan*	*Canis*

According to the chart, which two organisms are most closely related?

A   organisms 1 and 2

B   organisms 2 and 3

C   organisms 1 and 4

D   organisms 3 and 4

DISCUSSION

Choice C is the correct answer. The organisms with the most subdivisions in common are the closest.

LESSON 39

Predictions, Inferences, and Conclusions

Key Words..........

Inference
Conclusion
Prediction

It can sometimes be confusing to differentiate among observations, inferences, and predictions because they are so closely related. An observation is the act of acquiring information through the senses or through measurements. When you make an inference, you arrive at a logical explanation based on observation. A prediction is a statement about what will happen in the future based on observations in the past and present.

In order to find answers to questions, scientists use observations, data, and analysis to make inferences, conclusions, and predictions.

An **inference** is a deduction or assumption based on observation and prior knowledge. For example, a scientist might see that fish are dying in lakes near a power plant and infer that some factory byproduct is making the fish sick. An inference might lead to a hypothesis and may impact the design of an experiment.

Unlike an inference, a **conclusion** is a statement that explains the relationship between the variables of an experiment. A conclusion is derived directly from the data. Generally, a conclusion should review the cause-and-effect relationship between the independent and dependent variables established in the hypothesis.

A **prediction** is a statement suggesting what might happen in the future. A prediction is based on patterns in data and experiences. For instance, a student noted that the leaves on the trees turn brilliant colors after a warm, wet summer. She might then make a prediction that after a warm, wet summer the leaves will turn brilliant colors.

A prediction can suggest how to organize an experiment. A conclusion might also lead to a prediction. If the prediction comes true, it supports the conclusion. In 1915, Albert Einstein used his general theory of relativity to predict that massive objects bend light. When this result was observed during a solar eclipse in 1919, it overwhelmingly supported his theory.

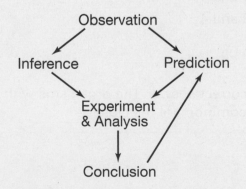

140

Throughout most of this unit, you have been learning how to design experiments to obtain reliable data. You have also learned how to organize, order, classify, and analyze the data. Now you must consider how to communicate your results to others.

One of the most important points in communicating your results is being able to summarize your data. One investigation may produce many pages of data. You want to be able to review the main points of the data without expecting others to read through every detail of your work.

In your summary, it is important that you explain scientific concepts. To accomplish this, you might use descriptive writing. You might also include illustrations and diagrams. And, if the situation permits, you may also need to describe your investigation orally.

Someone reviewing your work may benefit from seeing exactly what you observed. If this is the case, you may include photographs or digital images of your setup and results. If the setup is too large to view in a summary, you may be able to include a scale drawing.

At the end of your summary, you should describe your conclusions. As you do so, explain how you reached those conclusions as a result of combining many ideas and observations. In this way, a reader will not only know what you have learned, but how you have learned it. Presenting a summary in this manner makes your conclusions easier to understand and accept.

Just as you use tools to conduct an investigation, you might use tools to communicate your results. For example, computers or graphing calculators can assist you in drawing graphs or creating spreadsheets to include in your summary.

It is important to point out relationships identified through your research. Whenever explaining concepts or principles, be sure to point out similarities and differences between your results and the results of other researchers.

Whenever a question involves a graph or other diagram, make sure you know what is being represented before you attempt to answer the question. In this case, read the labels describing the axes and the lines being graphed.

EXAMPLE QUESTION

A researcher for a cosmetics company is studying a new mixture of acne treatments. The mixture contains ingredients from two existing creams—A and B. She hypothesizes that the new mixture, C, will fight pimples better than either of the previous creams. The data from an investigation are shown below.

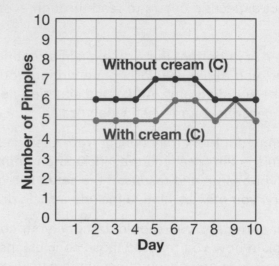

Based on the data, which action should the researcher take?

A She should confirm the hypothesis.

B She should reject the hypothesis completely.

C She should modify the hypothesis to indicate that the new cream is better than one of the existing creams.

D She should modify the hypothesis to describe a new cream based on all three of the creams.

DISCUSSION

The data show that the new cream performs better than A, but not better than B. Therefore, she should modify the hypothesis accordingly and conduct a new investigation. Choice C is the correct answer. Choice A is incorrect because the data do not confirm the hypothesis. Choice B is not correct because the hypothesis is partly correct. Choice D is incorrect because it describes a completely new hypothesis.

LESSON 40

Bias in Scientific Investigations

Sometimes a conclusion may seem pretty clear at first glance. But it is the job of the scientist to be skeptical. That does not mean a scientist must be negative, but that he or she must not blindly accept the conclusions of others. Instead, the scientist must critique arguments in case they are based on faulty or misleading information or an incomplete use of mathematical data. Consider the following example:

A scientist noticed that her children grew up to be nearsighted. She recalled that they slept with a night-light when they were young. She believed that sleeping with a light on prevented their eyes from resting, which led to the condition later in life. To test her hypothesis, she interviewed a number of parents and children. She concluded that children who slept with a night-light did indeed become nearsighted.

Another researcher was skeptical of this conclusion. After reviewing the procedure and the people interviewed for the investigation, this researcher made a discovery. Adults who are nearsighted tend to use night-lights more often than parents with normal vision. The reason is that adults who are nearsighted need night-lights to assist them in attending to their children during the night. Therefore it may simply be that the children who slept with night-lights became nearsighted as a result of genetics—their parents were also nearsighted—rather than because they slept with a night-light.

In a laboratory investigation in school, there is often one solution to a problem. In real situations, however, there are often multiple solutions. Scientists must incorporate many pieces of information in order to decide which solution to accept.

In this example, the original conclusions were based on a faulty experimental design. This is one important reason why scientists must include their design and procedure in a summary. Without realizing it, a scientist might design an experiment that leads to an expected conclusion or might interpret the data in only one way. The predisposition to a particular idea or conclusion is known as bias. By allowing other scientists with different views to repeat the investigation or to review their data, scientists can develop a more objective and reliable conclusion.

Even without bias, scientists have a responsibility to be truthful in reporting the methods and outcomes of their investigations. Regardless of what a scientist hopes to prove in an experiment, scientists must present their findings in a truthful manner. They must allow other scientists to review their work and they must make the public aware of their results, because the results of many scientific investigations have tremendous impacts on society.

There have been many occasions in which researchers announced results that were soon discarded because they were unable to present a method of replicating them. Consider, for example, scientists researching new treatments for disease. If the treatments are successful, the scientists not only will be able to improve the quality of life for many people, but they also stand to gain considerable financial reward. The zeal to be successful, then, might cause researchers to hide or misrepresent negative results. In the 1990s, studies involving curing disease through gene therapy were halted when it was discovered that several deaths and illnesses related to the studies had not been reported.

As you may have realized by now, important qualities that scientists should bring to research include curiosity, honesty, and openness. It is curiosity that leads a scientist to ask questions that are explored through the investigations. Honesty and openness are required to make the conclusions of research credible throughout the scientific community and society.

EXAMPLE QUESTION

A scientist is conducting research toward the goal of protecting the atmosphere from pollution. He discovers information that a large section of Arctic ice has melted. This discovery could be used as evidence of global warming. However, records indicated that this melted region has melted and refrozen several times during the last century. This discovery, then, might hinder his argument that increased pollution in the atmosphere was to blame. The scientist wants to report only the current appearance of the melted region rather than its history as well. Why must he report all of his findings?

_____

_____

_____

_____

DISCUSSION

Although his intentions may be good, the scientists should not hide or alter findings in order to make his argument stronger. The fact that his discovery does not support his argument means that he may have to change his approach or look for other evidence. If he hides information, he is discrediting not only his theory but himself as well.

New Ideas in Science

The general public is not the only group to reject scientific discoveries—sometimes it is the scientific community that is reluctant to consider new findings. For more than a century, Galileo and Kepler were among the few scientists that accepted Copernicus' theory. Eventually, however, other scientists researched the same topic and added to it. Most theories in science are the result of contributions from many different people.

Has your scientific view of the world changed in a major way during your lifetime? Probably not. In your study of science, you have always been taught that the Sun is in the center of the solar system, that matter is made up of atoms, and that living things are made up of cells.

That was not always the case. At some points in history, there have been major shifts in scientific views. For example, people were once quite sure that Earth was flat and that it was at the center of the universe. At some point, careful observations about the natural world caused someone to recognize that the common belief was incorrect.

When Copernicus proposed the idea that the Sun was in the center of the solar system, he was met with harsh criticism, because religious beliefs at the time insisted that Earth had to be the center of the universe. Because his idea did not mesh well with mainstream ideas at the time, he was ridiculed. Over time, however, his theory was judged in terms of how well it explained observations and how effective it was at predicting new findings. Eventually, it was accepted.

Changes in scientific thought are not always as dramatic as those described. In fact, more often the changes that take place in the scientific body of knowledge are small modifications of what is already known. For example, scientists once believed that stomach ulcers were caused entirely by stress. This idea has been replaced with the idea that ulcers are caused by bacterial infections. While this does not change anyone's view of the world, it does provide new information about how something in the world works and gives scientists new questions to explore.

Over time, ideas are judged according to how they fit with other theories and how well they explain observations. Only over time can such ideas be tested to find how successful they are at predicting new outcomes. Scientists must be prepared to change or support scientific ideas based on an accumulation of evidence. What does that mean? That if you are a scientist, you must be willing to let go of a belief once evidence shows it to be untrue. Similarly, you may need to support a belief that may seem difficult to believe if the evidence upholds it.

EXAMPLE QUESTION

From the time of the ancient Romans until the late 19th century, it was generally believed that some life forms arose spontaneously from nonliving matter. This theory was known as spontaneous generation. In 1668, the Italian scientist Francesco Redi set out to disprove the theory. He placed meat in a variety of flasks, some open to the air, some sealed completely, and others covered with gauze. Over time he observed that maggots appeared in the open flasks. He concluded that the maggots did not appear spontaneously, but that their eggs had been laid by flies. The maggots appeared on the meat the flies could reach. Despite his experiment, the belief in spontaneous generation continued until a more conclusive experiment was conducted by Louis Pasteur in 1859.

Based on the information above, which statement is true?

A Spontaneous generation was difficult to disprove because it always occurs under certain conditions.

B Redi could not disprove spontaneous generation because he changed too many variables at one time.

C The theory of spontaneous generation was quickly disproved once Redi showed it was not true.

D Almost 200 years passed before the theory of spontaneous generation was laid to rest.

DISCUSSION

The correct answer is choice D. In fact, 191 years passed between Redi's experiment and Pasteur's experiment.

The development of a new theory is not a failure in science. In fact, it is an achievement. Science is a never-ending process of asking questions and making observations about the natural world. Although one theory may fit most observations, a new theory is sometimes necessary to fit some new observations.

In English class, you may have learned to identify the details of a passage. Do the same for science articles. The details provide information about when events occurred, what happened, and who was involved.

LESSON
42

Science and Society

Key Word

Technology

As you have learned, science is a process. Through science, people can ask questions about the natural world and then find answers to those questions in an organized, efficient manner. The goal of science is knowledge. Sometimes the knowledge acquired through science is applied to develop a product or process. The application of science is called **technology**.

Science and technology are related, but they are not the same. The chart below will help you to see how science and technology are alike and how they are different. Each one can be broken down into four major stages.

Scientific Inquiry	Technological Design
Scientific Question A question about the natural world is identified.	*Problem Identification* A problem or a need is identified.
Hypothesis An educated guess is made to answer the scientific question.	*Solution Design* A product is proposed to solve the problem or fill the need identified.
Experiment The hypothesis is tested through observation or controlled experiment.	*Implementation* The solution or product is developed and tested in a real setting.
Conclusion The results, or data, from the experiment are analyzed in order to draw a conclusion about whether or not the hypothesis was supported.	*Evaluation* The results of the implementation are analyzed to determine whether or not the solution or product successfully solved the problem or filled the need.

Notice that the outcome of science is information, whereas the outcome of technology is a product. Just as a hypothesis is interpreted according to the data of an experiment, a technological product must be evaluated in terms of its success.

In some cases, for example, a technological problem creates a demand for new scientific knowledge. Doctors trying to replace a person's faulty heart might be limited in the artificial parts they have. This will create a demand to better understand the heart as well as the materials that can be used within the body.

In other cases, new technologies make it possible for scientists to extend their research in a way that advances science. Early astronomers reached their conclusions by making observations of the sky using their unaided eyes. The invention of the telescope afforded astronomers an opportunity to gather a vast amount of new information about the universe. Similarly, the invention of the microscope made it possible to study organisms in terms of their cells and the structures within cells.

Telescope   Binoculars   Microscope   Hand lens

Although scientists are not responsible for making decisions for society, they are responsible for providing people with the information they need to make decisions. When the public is evaluating an endeavor, such as the space station or the disposal of radioactive wastes, it needs to understand both the risks and the benefits. Scientists can bring information to the public so that people can assess the possible causes and effects from such decisions.

Scientific ideas and technological advancements can have major impacts on society. One way is by impacting the quality of life. The knowledge of science and the products of technology can improve health care by developing new treatments and prevention for diseases and medical conditions. In a similar way, they can develop a better understanding of environmental systems and how to protect and conserve them.

Another way science and technology affect society is by impacting the expense of funds. Consider the International Space Station, which is a satellite in space in which researchers from around the world can conduct experiments and make observations about events that occur in space. What does this have to do with you? A lot! For one thing, the United States spends a tremendous amount of money each year on the construction and maintenance of the space station. That means that when you begin to pay taxes, some of your money will be spent on research projects such as the space station. In addition, products that result from this research will eventually make their way into your life.

The advances of science and technology are always wonderful things that make people happy. Right? Not necessarily. Recall that scientific ideas are evaluated in terms of the values of the society to which they are proposed. The same is true for technology. The value of a technology is different depending on the people involved and the time during which the technology is presented. Neither pursuit can make ethical decisions. Only people can decide what to do with the information and technology. Just because a technological design makes something possible does not necessarily mean that the technology should be used. Society as a whole must debate the emotional, social, economic, and political issues related to new technologies.

You have concentrated on the pursuit of biological investigations throughout this book. All scientific disciplines, however, have an important impact on society. Areas of scientific study share the same goals and use of the scientific method. They differ, however, in their specific aims, methods, and subject matter. Chemistry, for example, attempts to understand the structure of matter, while geology studies Earth's natural processes. Physics studies the nature and interactions of matter and energy, while biology tries to untangle the structure and interactions among living things.

EXAMPLE QUESTION

Scientists have discovered ways to clone, or make exact copies of organisms using a single cell. Which of the following questions will scientists be unable to answer in their cloning research?

A   Can every type of organism be cloned?

B   Are there any errors in the genetic material of a cloned organism?

C   Does cloning require certain types of cells?

D   Should humans be cloned?

DISCUSSION

Scientists can discover new information about how natural processes work. Although scientists may have their personal views, the scientific method does not allow for moral or ethical decisions. As a result, scientists are not the ultimate deciders of whether or not cloning should occur. Society as a whole must make that decision. Choice D is the correct answer.

Review

1 Mara investigated a strain of bacteria often used to decompose oil in oil spills at sea. She placed equal numbers of the bacteria in three different salt solutions: 0.5%, 1.5%, and 2.5%. She kept all of the solutions in a lighted incubator set at 22°C. After three days, she took the samples from the solutions and counted the number of bacteria in each sample. What question is Mara investigating?

A Do oil-decomposing bacteria grow well in a warm, lighted environment?

B Does salt concentration affect the growth of this strain of bacteria?

C Are these bacteria the best strain to use in cleaning oil spills at sea?

D Do bacteria in salt solutions grow best at 22°C?

2 A scientist is increasing the concentration of reactants in a chemical reaction in order to find out how they affect the rate of the reaction. In this experiment, what is the rate of the reaction?

F hypothesis   **H** dependent variable

G manipulated variable   **J** control

3 Katie uses these tools to measure a piece of metal. What is the density of the sample?

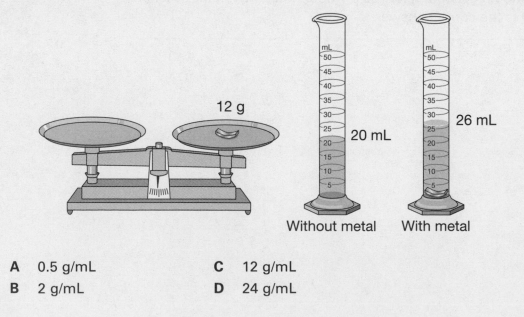

12 g

20 mL

26 mL

Without metal   With metal

A 0.5 g/mL   **C** 12 g/mL

B 2 g/mL   **D** 24 g/mL

4 You see the symbol shown here in the discussion of your laboratory procedure. What does this symbol tell you?

F The experiment will involve dead animals.

G You will be lighting a dangerous flame.

H You will be using poisonous chemicals.

J You should not conduct this experiment inside.

5 A researcher is conducting an investigation to find out how the amount of carbon dioxide in the air affects the rate of photosynthesis. She encloses 10 plants individually and changes the amount of carbon dioxide in the air around each one. She measures the amount of oxygen produced by each one as a way to study photosynthesis. Which is the best way to compare the photosynthetic activity of the plants?

A diagram

B line graph

C circle graph

D bar graph

6 Simon is mixing paint. The can says to use 3 cans of water for every 2 cans of concentrated paint mix. He is using 6 cans of concentrated paint mix. How many cans of water should he use?

F 2

H 6

G 3

J 9

7 Tom investigated whether salt raises the boiling point of water. He put 2 gallons of water at 20°C and 2 cups of salt in a pot, heated it over a flame, and measured the temperature when the water reached a rolling boil. He repeated the experiment three times and recorded the same result each time. He concluded that salt raises the boiling point of water by 5°C. Where did Tom err in his experimental design?

A   He did not conduct the trials at the same time.

B   He waited until the water reached a rolling boil.

C   He should have repeated the measurement several more times.

D   He did not boil a pot of water without salt.

8 Which of the following is the most useful way to classify chemical elements into groups?

F   according to the state of matter at room temperature

G   according to the first letter of the chemical symbol

H   according to the number of neutrons in the nucleus

J   according to the year it was discovered

9 Melinda is investigating the formation and importance of fossil fuels. She made a circle graph to describe the relative percentages of different energy sources used to produce electricity in the United States. Based on her graph, which of the following statements is true?

Energy Sources in the U.S.

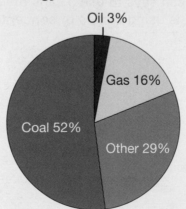

A   Oil accounts for nearly half of all the energy used to produce electricity.

B   Gas accounts for the least amount of energy used to produce electricity.

C   Coal accounts for more than half of all the energy used to produce electricity.

D   Together, oil, coal, and gas account for more than 90% of all the energy used to produce electricity.

154

10   Read the following passage carefully. Then answer the question.

Alfred Wegener was a scientist who first proposed the idea that the continents drift slowly. He based his beliefs on such observations as the shapes of coastlines, the presence of similar fossils on different continents, and the continuation of mountain chains from one continent to another. During his life, Wegener's theory was largely discredited by scientists of the day. Years later, when new instruments were invented that enabled researchers to study the ocean floor, the researchers discovered that Wegener was indeed correct and identified additional information about continents and the plates on which they are located.

How do new technologies further the pursuit of science?

Write your answer in your Answer Book.

_____

_____

_____

_____

_____

_____

_____

Maryland Coach, High School Biology Posttest

Posttest

1 Which organic compound is shown in the diagram?

A starch

B carbohydrate

C protein

D lipid

2 Organic molecules that carry genetic information from one generation to the next are

F carbohydrates

G minerals

H lipids

J nucleic acids

3 Jeda placed a plastic bottle of water in the freezer to make it cold. When she returned to get the bottle, she discovered that it had cracked. Which property of water is responsible for this?

A Water is an excellent solvent.

B Ice is less dense than liquid water.

C Water is a nonpolar molecule.

D Water releases and absorbs energy quickly.

4 Magnesium and calcium are examples of inorganic substances that the human body needs in small amounts. What are these substances called?

F   vitamins

G   minerals

H   lipids

J   carbohydrates

5 Sodium ions are found at a lower concentration inside a cell than outside a cell. These ions move from areas of high concentration to areas of low concentration. What is this process called?

A   diffusion

B   active transport

C   osmosis

D   gradation

6 The diagram shows four different cells in solutions of particles. The membranes of the cells are permeable to water but not to the particles. Which cell will shrink immediately after being placed in the solution?

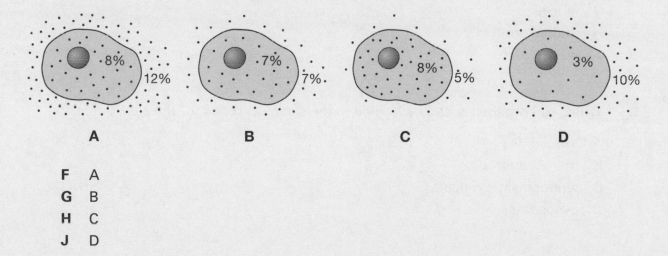

F   A

G   B

H   C

J   D

7 The pH of blood is relatively neutral. It is neither an acid nor a base. You would expect the pH of blood to be close to

A   0

B   4

C   7

D   14

Directions Use the diagram of the animal cell to answer Numbers 8, 9, and 10.

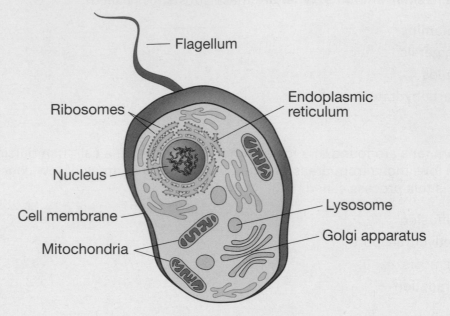

8   In which organelles does aerobic cellular respiration occur?

   F   ribosomes
   G   nuclei
   H   mitochondria
   J   vacuole

9   Which cell organelles can be likened to the clean-up crews for the cell?

   A   ribosomes
   B   mitochondria
   C   endoplasmic reticula
   D   lysosomes

10   What is the role of the tail-like structure extending from the back of the cell?

   F   It is used to capture food.
   G   It is used to release wastes.
   H   It is used during reproduction.
   J   It used to enable the cell to move.

11 A single-celled organism is exposed to a toxin. What will most likely happen to the organism?

    A It will weaken or die.

    B It will grow larger and flourish.

    C It will absorb and feed off the toxin.

    D It will divide to become a multicellular organism.

12 As surface temperatures rise, the rate at which water evaporates increases. How might a period of high temperatures affect the water cycle?

    F It would increase the size of the droplets that form through condensation.

    G It would increase the amount of water that leaves Earth's surface.

    H It would increase the amount of water that seeps underground.

    J It would increase the amount of precipitation.

13 The diagram summarizes the nitrogen cycle in a particular ecosystem.

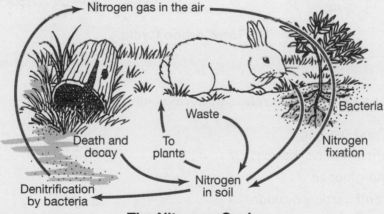

The Nitrogen Cycle

Based on this information, what happens to the nitrogen in a rabbit's body when it dies?

    A The nitrogen is broken down and destroyed.

    B The nitrogen is trapped and removed from the cycle.

    C The nitrogen is converted into a usable form through nitrogen fixation.

    D The nitrogen is broken down and returned to the cycle through denitrification.

14 What is the source of energy for photosynthesis?

    F water in the soil

    G light from the sun

    H compounds in leaves

    J heat released by decomposers

Directions **Use the diagram of the carbon cycle to answer Numbers 15 and 16.**

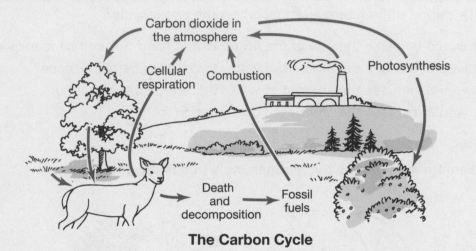

The Carbon Cycle

15 Which of these products are released during cellular respiration?

    A glucose and oxygen

    B carbon dioxide and water

    C water and glucose

    D oxygen and carbon dioxide

16 Which of these changes would lead to an increase in the removal of carbon dioxide from the atmosphere?

    F increase in respiration

    G decrease in photosynthesis

    H decrease in manufacturing

    J increase in the number of trees

17 An organism that conducts chemosynthesis is different from an organism that conducts photosynthesis because it

A does not require energy to produce food

B is a consumer rather than a producer of food

C uses inorganic compounds as a source of energy

D lives in isolation without other organisms around it

18 Which process takes place in the presence of oxygen and produces nearly twenty times as much ATP as glycolysis alone?

F mitosis

G photosynthesis

H aerobic respiration

J lactic acid fermentation

19 The building blocks of DNA are

A genes

B nucleotides

C amino acids

D ribosomes

20
• How are the processes of meiosis and mitosis alike?

• How are these processes different?

• How are both processes related to fertilization?

Write your answer in your Answer Book.

_____

_____

_____

_____

_____

_____

21 The cell of an earthworm has 36 chromosomes. How many chromosomes are in the sex cells of an earthworm?

    A   9
    B   18
    C   36
    D   72

Directions Use the information and Punnett square to answer Numbers 22 and 23.

In pea plants, the allele for purple flower color (P) is dominant to the allele for white flower color (p). The Punnett square below shows the alleles of two pea plants that were crossed.

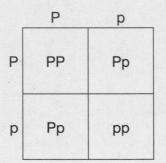

22 What is the probable percentage of the offspring from this cross that will have white flowers?

    F   25%
    G   50%
    H   75%
    J   100%

23 Suppose two of the offspring are crossed. If all of their offspring have white flowers, what must have been the genotypes of the plants that were crossed?

    A   PP × PP
    B   Pp × Pp
    C   PP × Pp
    D   pp × pp

24 The pedigree shows the pattern of inheritance for a particular genetic disorder.

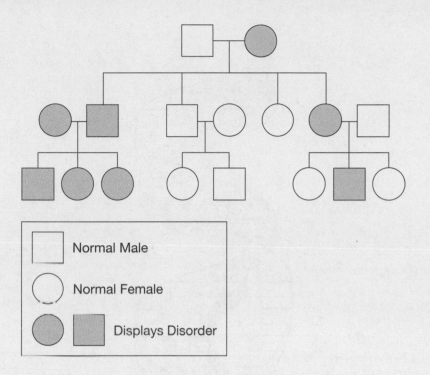

According to the pedigree, this disease is caused by a

F recessive gene that is sex-linkcd

G dominant gene that is sex-linked

H recessive gene that is not sex-linked

J dominant gene that is not sex-linked

25 In a strand of DNA, which base pairs with thymine (T)?

A uracil (U)

B adenine (A)

C guanine (G)

D cytosine (C)

26 A student has created the following diagram to show part of a process that occurs in a cell nucleus.

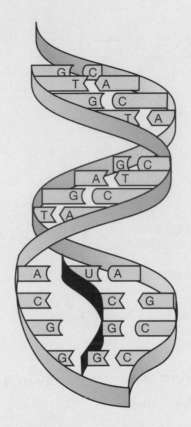

Explain what is happening in the diagram and how this process is important to the cell.

Write your answer in your Answer Book.

_____

_____

_____

_____

_____

_____

_____

27 A group of scientists were looking for a way to produce human insulin outside the human body. Toward this end, they inserted the gene responsible for producing human insulin into a sheep. This is an example of

    A natural selection

    B genetic engineering

    C fermentation

    D evolution

Directions   Use the information and diagram to answer Numbers 28 and 29.

The diagram below shows the DNA of a cell being copied before the cell divides. An error that occurred during this process is indicated by an asterisk (*) in the diagram.

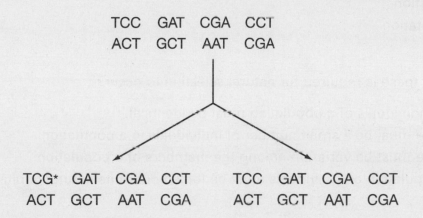

28 When the DNA in the diagram was copied, one of the bases was changed. As a result, the copied DNA has a

    F mutation

    G replication

    H translation

    J recombination

29 The sequence TCC changed to TCG while the DNA was copied. The result will be the production of the wrong

    A cytoplasm

    B lipid

    C carbohydrate

    D protein

30 How does a mutation in an organism's DNA most often affect the organism?

    F It changes the DNA to RNA.

    G It becomes the norm for the population.

    H It makes the organism better adapted to its environment.

    J It changes the proteins produced by the organism's cells.

31 The hands of koalas have a large gap between the first and second fingers. This structure enables koalas to climb trees and grip onto branches easily. This characteristic is important to koalas because they feed mainly on eucalyptus leaves that they reach by climbing trees. Which term best describes this characteristic?

    A recombination

    B homeostasis

    C mutation

    D adaptation

32 Which of these is required for natural selection to occur?

    F All individuals of a population must be identical.

    G There must be a small number of individuals in a population.

    H There must be variation among the members of a population.

    J A population of individuals must be forced out of its natural habitat.

33 A certain bird species feeds on the seeds of a particular tree. A drought causes the outer covering of the seeds to become thicker and harder over time. After many generations, what is the most likely effect of this change on the birds?

    A The birds will have stronger beaks.

    B Some of the birds will be larger and some will be smaller.

    C There will be no physical or behavioral change in the birds.

    D All of the birds will starve and the species will become extinct.

34 During a research expedition, researchers discovered an organism that has never been observed before. It is a new species of jellyfish that they nicknamed "Big Red."

- What kinds of evidence could the researchers use to determine the evolutionary relationship between the jellyfish and other organisms?

- How would they use this evidence to demonstrate evolutionary relationships?

Write your answer in your Answer Book.

_____

_____

_____

_____

_____

_____

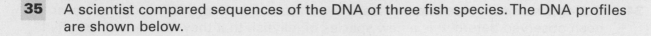

35 A scientist compared sequences of the DNA of three fish species. The DNA profiles are shown below.

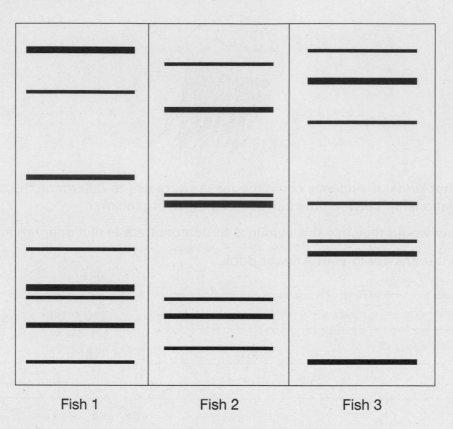

Fish 1   Fish 2   Fish 3

What can the scientist learn from these DNA profiles?

A   the number of individuals in each population of fish

B   how closely the fishes are related to one another

C   the total number of genes in each fish

D   the diets of the ancestors of each fish

36 The chart below shows the classification of four different organisms.

	1 Greenland Shark	2 Angel Shark	3 Prickly Shark	4 Sawshark
Kingdom	Animalia	Animalia	Animalia	Animalia
Phylum	Chordata	Chordata	Chordata	Chordata
Class	Chondrichthyes	Chondrichthyes	Chondrichthyes	Chondrichthyes
Order	Squaliformes	Squatiniformes	Squaliformes	Pristiophoriformes
Family	Somniosus	Squatinidae	Echinorhinidae	Pristiophoridae

According to the chart, which two organisms are most closely related?

F   organisms 1 and 2

G   organisms 2 and 3

H   organisms 1 and 3

J   organisms 3 and 4

37 The living things in an Antarctic ecosystem are strongly affected by changes in physical factors such as temperature, winds, current, salinity, and ice cover. In this ecosystem, phytoplankton are the main producers. A species of zooplankton, called krill, are the primary consumers. To some extent, fish, penguins, seals, whales, and other animals of the ecosystem depend on krill to survive.

Which of these is a biotic factor in this ecosystem?

A   the amount of ice at any given time

B   the amount of salt in the ocean water

C   the temperature of the air and water

D   the size of the krill population

38 The oxpecker is an African bird that can be found living among oxen and other large mammals. Some research shows that the oxpecker helps the oxen by removing ticks and other parasites. Other research suggests that the birds actually peck the oxen in order to feed off the oxen's blood.

- The relationship between the oxpecker and the oxen may be an example of commensalisms or it may be predation. What is the difference between the two relationships?

- Give another example of each type of relationship.

Write your answer in your Answer Book.

_____

_____

_____

_____

_____

39 A student is studying how birds are adapted to their environments. Which bird foot belongs to a bird that thrives in a water environment?

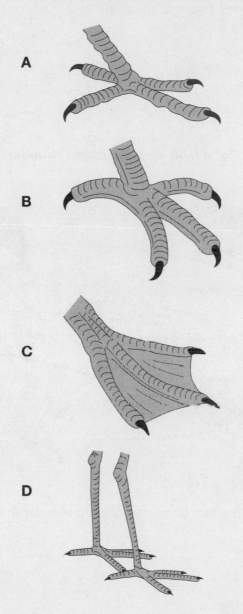

A

B

C

D

A A
B B
C C
D D

40 Epiphytes are plants that use other plants for structure as they grow. In this relationship, the epiphyte benefits without benefiting or harming the other plant. Which term best describes this relationship?

   F   commensalism
   G   parasitism
   H   predation
   J   mutualism

Directions   Use the diagram of a food web to answer Numbers 41 and 42.

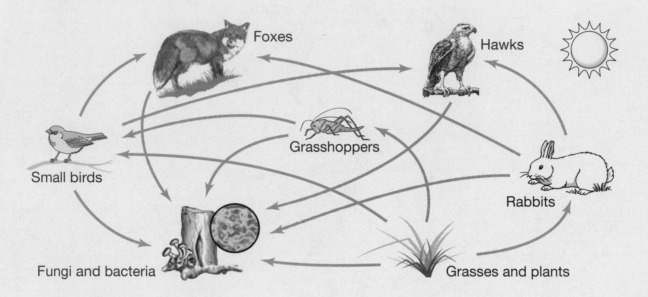

41 Which of these organisms is a primary consumer from the terrestrial food web shown here?

   A   fungus
   B   grass
   C   grasshopper
   D   hawk

42 Suppose a disease strikes, killing most of the hawks. How will the ecosystem be affected?

   F   The number of plants will decrease.
   G   The number of foxes will increase.
   H   The populations of fungi and bacteria will decrease.
   J   The rabbit and bird populations will increase in size.

43 The diagram shows a food chain from a marine food web. What is the role of algae in this ecosystem?

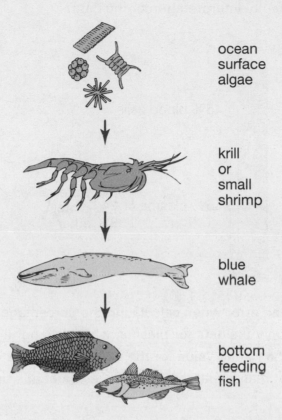

ocean
surface
algae

krill
or
small
shrimp

blue
whale

bottom
feeding
fish

A producer

B consumer

C decomposer

D carnivore

44 When considering technological changes, society must consider the trade-offs between using and not using the technology. What is a direct disadvantage of expanding human communities into undeveloped land?

F It can alter the genetic information in communities of animals living on that land.

G It can destroy animal habitats, causing some animals to become endangered.

H It can cause new species to develop in response to the change.

J It can increase the size of the human population on Earth.

45 A student is investigating the composition of blood. Based on the data in the diagram, the student states that almost all of blood is made up of water. Why is this statement based on a faulty interpretation of the data?

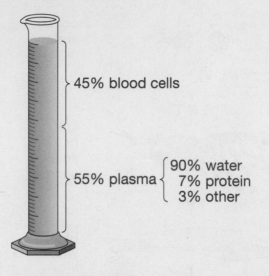

45% blood cells

55% plasma { 90% water
7% protein
3% other

A The student made an error when calculating the percentage of water.

B The student used only the data for plasma, which is a portion of blood.

C The student read the wrong value for the percentage of water in the blood.

D The student did not realize that the percentages must add up to a total of 100.

46 A student conducted an investigation to study plants. The setup is shown in the diagram.

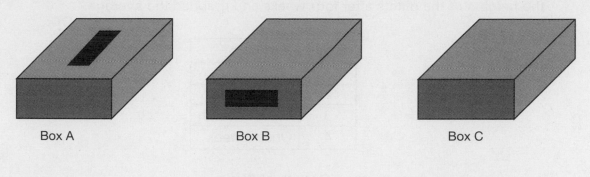

Box A   Box B   Box C

Plant A   Plant B   Plant C

What question is the student most likely investigating?

F How do plants grow in small spaces?

G Will plants grow taller with fertilizer?

H How does light affect the growth of plants?

J How are plants affected by the amount of water they receive?

47 A student wants to determine if a cell is a plant cell or an animal cell. Which of these would be the best tool for the student to use?

A thermometer

B mass balance

C compound microscope

D graduated cylinder

48 Dr. Velez investigated the effects of fertilizer on the growth of plants. She grew four groups in identical conditions, except as described in the table below. She recorded the heights of the plants after four weeks and graphed the average.

Group	Fertilizer
1	None
2	Once a month
3	Twice a month
4	Once a week

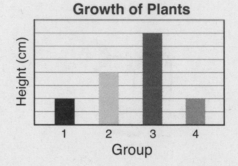

Growth of Plants

- What is a testable hypothesis for this experiment?
- Define a control group and identify the control group in this experiment.
- What are the dependent and manipulated variables in this experiment?
- What conclusion can she reach based on the data?

Write your answer in your Answer Book.

_____

_____

_____

_____

_____

49 Which of the following actions is a safe lab practice?

A Wear goggles only when using a Bunsen burner.

B Tilt test tubes away from you when heating them.

C Taste a chemical to identify it before breathing in the vapors.

D Substitute chemicals when they are in the same group from the periodic table.

50 In medieval Europe, farmers stored grains in barns with thatched roofs. As the roofs grew older, they would often leak. The moisture would cause the grain to become moldy. At the same time, mice appeared. People concluded that mice were produced by moldy grain. How might they have used the scientific method to test their conclusion?

Write your answer in your Answer Book.

_____

_____

_____

_____

_____

51 A few turtles move to an uninhabited island and survive. After hundreds of years, a meteor strikes the island. Some of the turtles survive this disaster. Which graph best shows how the turtle population rises and falls from the time of the first habitation to a few hundred years after the meteor strike?

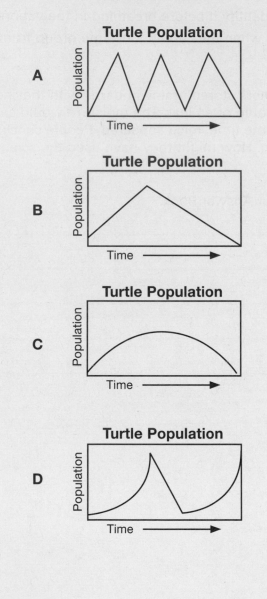

A A
B B
C C
D D

52 This graph shows the solubility of a solid at different temperatures. How many grams of solute would you expect to dissolve at 120°C?

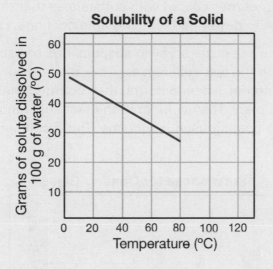

Solubility of a Solid

F   13

G   28

H   41

J   100

Directions Use the information in this selection to answer Numbers 53, 54, and 55.

In industry, glass is sometimes coated with substances that retard bacterial growth. Some chemical engineers developed four possible coatings, called T1, T2, T3, and T4.

To test the coatings, the scientists sprayed suspensions of bacteria in water onto the glass plates coated with the test substances. After the surfaces dried, they put the plates on a nutrient material. After 48 hours, they counted the number of bacterial colonies on each glass plate. They compared the test substances to a material, N, a commercially available coating used in industry. The results are graphed below.

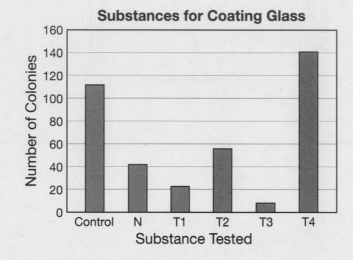

53 Which substances merit further research?

A T1, T2, T3, and T4

B T1 and T3

C T2 and T4

D T3 only

54 Which of the test substances promotes bacterial adherence?

F T1

G T2

H T3

J T4

55   Which choice would be the best control for the research?

   A   a glass plate coated with N
   B   a glass plate coated with a mixture of T1, T2, T3, and T4
   C   a glass plate with no coating
   D   a metal plate with no coating

Glossary

Abiotic factor   A nonliving component of an ecosystem.

Accuracy   The description of a measurement that is close to the accepted standard value for the measurement.

Acid   A compound that tastes sour, turns litmus paper red, and reacts with metals to produce hydrogen gas.

Active transport   The movement of molecules against a concentration gradient with the expense of energy.

Adaptation   A beneficial trait that enables an organism to survive and reproduce.

Aerobic   A process that takes place in the presence of oxygen.

Allele   A gene that controls an alternative form of a genetic trait.

Amino acid   A compound containing carbon, hydrogen, oxygen, and nitrogen that serves as a building block of proteins.

Anaerobic   A process that takes place in the absence of oxygen.

Asexual reproduction   The production of offspring in which only one parent is required.

ATP   Adenosine triphosphate, which is a compound that stores energy.

Autosome   A chromosome that carries information for characteristics other than gender.

Base   A compound that tastes bitter, feels slippery, turns litmus paper blue, and does not react with metals.

Binary fission   A process through which a cell splits into two parts in such a way that each part receives one copy of the DNA.

Biotic factor   A living component of an ecosystem.

Carbohydrate   An organic compound consisting of carbon, hydrogen, and oxygen that is present in the cells of all living things.

Carbon cycle   The process through which carbon is used and recycled in nature.

Carnivore   An animal that eats meat in order to obtain energy.

Cell   The basic unit of structure and function in living things.

Cell cycle   A process that leads from the formation of a cell to the division of a cell.

Cell membrane   A thin boundary that surrounds a cell and acts as a barrier between the inside of the cell and the cell's environment.

Cell wall   A rigid structure that surrounds the cell membrane in the cells of plants, fungi, many protists, and most bacteria.

Cellular respiration   The process by which cells convert glucose and oxygen into carbon dioxide and water.

Chemosynthesis   The process through which organisms, such as species of archaebacteria, obtain carbon from carbon dioxide and energy from sulfur to produce organic molecules.

Chloroplast   An organelle found in plant cells that uses the sun's energy to make food during the process of photosynthesis.

Chromosome   DNA and protein that contains all the genes of a cell and that is coiled into a rod-shaped structure.

Cilium   One of many, short, hair-like projections that enables a cell to move or to move materials across itself.

Classifying   The process of arranging items into groups according to their similarities and differences.

Climax community   A diverse, mature community.

Cloning   A technique in which an organism is produced that is genetically identical to its parent.

Codon   A group of three nucleotides on mRNA that specifies an amino acid.

Commensalism   A symbiotic relationship in which one organism benefits without harming the other.

Concentration gradient   The difference in the concentration of side-by-side areas.

Conclusion   An interpretation based on research, experience, and data.

Condensation   The process through which a gas changes to a liquid as it loses thermal energy.

Consumer   An organism that must eat other organisms for food.

Control group   Part of an experiment that is not subjected to the variable so that it can be compared to the experimental group.

Cytoplasm   A fluid that surrounds the organelles in a cell.

Data   Numerical measurements or observations that are obtained during an investigation.

Decomposer   An organism that breaks down dead and decaying organic matter and returns nutrients and carbon to the environment.

Density   The mass of an object divided by its volume.

Dependent variable   The variable that measures the effects of changes in the independent variable.

Dichotomous key   A system of classification in which items are divided into groups based on whether or not they possess a given characteristic.

Diffusion   A form of passive transport in which molecules move from an area of higher concentration to an area of lower concentration.

DNA   Dexyribonucleic acid, which stores the genetic information that determines an organism's traits.

DNA fingerprint   The pattern produced when DNA fragments are separated by size and shape by gel electrophoresis.

Dominant   The description of an inherited trait that is expressed even if a different, recessive gene for the same characteristic is also inherited.

Ecological succession   The process by which an existing ecosystem is gradually and progressively replaced by another ecosystem.

Ecology   The study of the interactions among living things and their environment.

Ecosystem   All of the living and nonliving parts interacting in a given area. The interaction of all of the biotic and abiotic factors of an environment.

Endoplasmic reticulum   A system of folds and channels that are responsible for transporting materials throughout a cell.

Enzyme   A molecule that serves as a catalyst to speed up chemical reactions in living things.

Evaporation   A combination of physical and biological factors that affect an organism.

Evolution   Change over time.

Experimental group   A group for which a researcher deliberately changes a variable for the purposes of comparison to a control group.

Extinction   When all members of a species die out.

Flagellum   A tail-like cell structure that enables a cell to move or to move materials across itself.

Fossil   The remains, tracks, or other evidence of a once-living thing preserved in rock, earth, or amber.

Gene   A segment of DNA that codes for a protein and that determines a single trait.

Gene splicing   The process of controlling genes for practical purposes by transferring a segment of DNA from one organism to another.

Genetic engineering   The process through which scientists transfer genes from one organism to another.

Genotype   The alleles that an organism inherits from its parents.

Germinal mutation   A change in the genetic material that affects a reproductive cell and is therefore passed on to offspring.

Glycolysis   A process that breaks down glucose into pyruvic acid in cellular respiration.

Golgi apparatus   The cell organelle responsible for transporting proteins and other materials.

Herbivore   An organism that feeds directly on producers for energy.

Heterozygous   The description of an organism that has a mixed pair of alleles for a trait.

Homeostasis   The state in which a natural system is balanced and tends to maintain that balance; the ability of a living thing to maintain the constant internal environment needed to function and survive.

Homologous chromosomes Chromosomes that are similar in size, shape, and genetic material.

Homologous structures   Structures that have a common origin but not necessarily a common function.

Homozygous   The description of an organism that has an identical pair of alleles for a trait.

Host   An organism on or in which a parasite lives.

Hypothesis   A possible, testable explanation to a scientific question.

Inference   A deduction or assumption based on observation.

Inheritable characteristic A characteristic that is passed on from one generation to the next through genetic information.

Kingdom The largest group in the classification system of organisms.

Limiting factor A resource in an ecosystem that controls the maximum size of the community that can survive in that ecosystem.

Lipid A waxy or oily compound, such as a fat, that is made of fatty acids.

Lysosome A small sac-like organelle that contains enzymes.

Manipulated variable The variable that is changed during a controlled experiment.

Meiosis The process through which the nucleus of a cell divides in such a way that the number of chromosomes is divided in half.

Messenger RNA (mRNA) The form of RNA that carries genetic information from the DNA in the nucleus to the ribosomes in the cytoplasm.

Mineral A naturally occurring inorganic substance that is needed by the body in trace amounts to make certain body structures and substances, and for normal nerve and muscle function.

Mitochondrion An organelle that is scattered throughout a cell, which produces much of the ATP made by a eukaryotic cell.

Mitosis The process through which a nucleus divides in two in such a way that each new cell receives a complete set of chromosomes.

Multicellular organism An organism that is made up of more than one cell; the cells are specialized to perform the functions required by the organism.

Mutalism A symbiotic relationship in which both organisms benefit.

Mutation A change in the genetic material of an organism.

Natural selection The theory that organisms with favorable traits are more likely to survive, reproduce, and pass on their adaptations to their offspring.

Niche The conditions in which the organisms in a species can live and the way the organisms use those conditions.

Nitrogen cycle The processes by which nitrogen moves through the living and nonliving parts of an ecosystem.

Nucleic acid A large complex molecule made up of carbon, hydrogen, oxygen, nitrogen, and phosphorus; contains the genetic information passed from one generation to the next.

Nucleotide A subunit of DNA consisting of a sugar, a phosphate, and a base.

Nucleus The center of an atom, which consists of protons and neutrons; The organelle that contains most of a cell's DNA and controls most of the cell's activities.

Omnivore An organism that eats both producers, such as plants, and consumers, such as animals.

Organ A group of related tissues that work together to perform a specific function in the body.

Organ system A group of related organs that work together to perform a specific function in the body.

Organelle A structure that performs a specialized function within a eukaryotic cell.

Osmosis Diffusion of water across a semipermeable membrane.

Parasite An organism that takes nourishment from and lives at the expense of its host.

Parasitism A symbiotic relationship in which one organism benefits at the expense of another.

Passive transport The movement of materials into and out of a cell without an expense of energy.

Pedigree A chart used to trace the inheritance of a specific trait through several generations in a family.

pH A measure of the acidity or basicity of a substance; a pH of less than 7 indicates an acid whereas a pH that is greater than 7 indicates a base.

pH scale A system of measurement that indicates whether a substance is an acid or a base.

Phenotype The characteristics of an organism as a result of its genotype.

Photosynthesis The process through which autotrophs use the energy of sunlight to convert carbon dioxide and water into sugar and oxygen.

Pioneer species The first, fast growing species that appear in an area following a disturbance or in a previously barren environment.

Plastid A cell organelle surrounded by two membranes and contain genetic material.

Polarity The existence of different regions of charge within a molecule, such as a water molecule.

Population A group of organisms of the same species that live together at the same time in a given area.

Precipitation The process through which moisture in the atmosphere falls to Earth's surface as rain, sleet, hail, or snow.

Precision The description of whether or not a measurement is obtained as a result of numerous repeated measurements.

Predator An animal that kills and eats another animal for food.

Prediction A statement about what is likely to happen in the future based on observations of events that have already occurred.

Prey An animal that is killed and eaten by a predator as food.

Probability The mathematical chance that an event will occur.

Producer An organism that is capable of producing food through photosynthesis or chemosynthesis.

Product One of the substances that forms during a chemical reaction.

Proportion Two equal ratios.

Protein A chain of amino acids that is used for such activities as building cells and controlling chemical reactions.

Protein synthesis The construction of proteins by linking chains of amino acids; occurs at ribosomes in the cytoplasm of a cell.

Punnett square A diagram used to identify possible combinations of dominant and recessive alleles in offspring.

Qualitative data   Information obtained through an investigation that can be described by words rather than numerical measurements.

Quantitative data   Information obtained through an investigation that can be described by numerical measurements.

Ratio   A relationship between two numbers.

Reactant   One of the substances that enters into a chemical reaction.

Recessive   The description of an inherited trait that is not expressed if an offspring receives the allele for the trait from only one parent.

Recombinant DNA   Pieces of DNA from two or more sources that are inserted into a new organism for replication.

Replication   The process through which DNA is copied.

Resource depletion   A process through which humans place environmental support systems at risk by overusing or polluting natural resources.

Ribosome   The organelle in which amino acids are linked together to form proteins.

Ribosomal RNA (rRNA)   The form of RNA that is an important component of ribosomes.

RNA   Ribonucleic acid, which translates information encoded in DNA and uses the information to build proteins.

Scavenger   An animal that feeds on the carcasses of dead animals.

Scientific method   A series of steps used to answer a question or solve a problem about the natural world.

Scientific notation   A shorthand method of writing very large or very small numbers using powers of 10.

Semipermeable   A property of cell membranes that means that some substances can pass through easily whereas others cannot.

Sex chromosome   A chromosome that determines the sex of an organism; X and Y chromosomes.

Sex-linked trait   A trait carried by an allele on a sex chromosome.

Sexual reproduction   Reproduction in which two parent cells join together to form a new individual.

Single-celled organism   An organism consisting of only one cell that carries out all of the functions needed for the organism to survive.

Solvent   A substance in which another substance, the solute, is dissolved to form a solution.

Somatic mutation   A change in DNA that occurs in a nonreproductive cell and will not be passed on to offspring.

Species   A group of organisms that share similar characteristics and can interbreed with one another to produce fertile offspring.

Symbiosis   An interdependent relationship between two organisms.

Technology   The practical application of science to create tools, machines, and other devices.

Theory   A scientific statement of what is believed to be true, supported by experimental evidence from repeated testing of related hypotheses.

Tissue A group of several different kinds of cells working together to perform a specific function.

Transcription A process that takes place in a cell where DNA acts as a template to create mRNA.

Transfer RNA (tRNA) The form of RNA that carries an amino acid to the ribosome during protein synthesis.

Translation A process that takes place in a cell where three base codes create amino acids.

Transpiration The loss of water through the openings (called stomata) in vascular plants.

Urbanization The process through which humans destroy ecosystems as they clear land for construction.

Vacuole A large, membrane-covered chamber that stores enzymes and wastes in a cell.

Variable The factor that differs among test groups in an experiment and is measured against a control.

Variation A difference from one individual to the next.

Vitamin An organic substance that is necessary in small amounts for the normal functioning of an organism but cannot be produced by the organism.

Water cycle The flow of water through the environment by means of evaporation, transpiration, condensation, and precipitation.